Better to Forget

by

MARGARET PARGETER

Harlequin Books

TORONTO • LONDON • NEW YORK • AMSTERDAM • SYDNEY

Original hardcover edition published in 1977
by Mills & Boon Limited

ISBN 0-373-02183-6

Harlequin edition published July 1978

CHAPTER ONE

IT struck Liza a long time afterwards that such a momentous day had begun as normally as any other. That the morning had been slightly more harassing than usual might have served as a sort of warning of worse to come if she had allowed herself time to stop and think about it, which of course she didn't; the Liza Deans of this world, herself at any rate, not being able to afford the luxury of such idle reflection. Or so Miss Russell, her immediate boss at the shop, who ruled with the proverbial iron hand, always gave her to understand.

To start with Liza slept in, her tiny bed-sitter being tucked so far into the rooftops of the high old terrace house in north London that if her alarm failed to function no other sound appeared to penetrate loudly enough to wake her up. Besides, although she would not have been prepared to confess it openly, she wasn't always so very keen to return to consciousness, to face the monotony of another dull day.

So, what with sleeping in and the ensuing rush to get herself ready in half the normal time, she had been all of ten minutes late, and Miss Russell, who managed the exclusive gowns department at Lathams, the huge store where Liza worked, had been displeased. Liza's hastily expressed regrets had made little impression.

'There are hundreds of girls who would give anything to be able to step into your shoes, my dear,' she had reproached Liza acidly, flatly disclaiming any interest in her feeble excuse. 'Let it happen once more, Miss Dean,' she had continued coldly, 'and I'm afraid you must look elsewhere for employment!'

Liza's almond green eyes had clouded with an almost visible despair, and she had made heavily underlined mental notes to buy a second alarm as she had rushed to remove her outdoor things. Miss Russell could be tart but, as usual, she was so right! No one was more aware than Liza how fortunate she had been on coming back to London after the death of her father, to have got a job here without any previous training whatsoever. Just because her landlady had felt sorry for her and had spoken to Miss Russell who was a distant relation. It had been a stroke of sheer good luck, Liza was convinced, being far too sceptical to believe one of the other girls, who had said at the time that it was because of her unusual attractiveness.

'A touch of class, that's what you've got, young Dean, and old Russell just can't resist it!' Chloe Eden had paused thoughtfully, her eyes on Liza's doubtful face, before adding observantly, 'I suppose that's why she's at the top of her particular tree—her ability to spot something she can use to the advantage of her beloved department.'

Which might make sense, only not, Liza was convinced, where she was concerned. A touch of class indeed! Chloe was apparently given to exaggeration. Yet thinking Chloe quite crazy hadn't stopped Liza from seeking, at the first opportunity, the nearest mirror. Even now Liza could recall how she had stared furtively at her own wide-eyed reflection, seeing nothing in her rather deprived-looking figure to justify Chloe's irrational opinion.

Liza's hair, a thick, dark red mop, had been cut extremely short because of the temperatures in the tropics from which she had just returned, and her naturally pale skin had been browned to almost matching tints by the heat of the sun. Miss Russell might imagine she had possibilities but, unconvinced, Liza had turned away.

Yet hadn't Miss Russell asked her almost immediately to let her hair grow longer, and advised her to seek advice about her skin? Liza, trembling before such impersonal but emphatic authority, hadn't dared refuse, but it was doubtful, six months later, if she really appreciated her new appearance. While she did not care to believe she was lacking in proper gratitude, her new image, if beautiful, seemed totally lacking in reality. However, she had reflected, so long as Miss Russell was satisfied, the ruthless disposal of her old carelessly untidy self probably didn't much matter.

Liza had sighed moodily that morning as she hung up her coat and quickly thrust a comb through her tangled hair. It might be more honest to admit that her lack of appreciation had little to do with Miss Russell. It was simply that she had never really fancied this particular kind of work in the first place, but it had been essential she did something. She had never imagined it would be so difficult to settle down. She supposed this might be because she had been too used to running around the world after her father. The father she had always called Dan, as when she was small she could never seem to pronounce Dad properly, and somehow the different version had stuck. Anyway, it was he who had always insisted he preferred it to anything else, even after Liza had grown up.

Compared to her life at the store, it had been a lot more fun roaming the world with him, helping him gather material for his books. It had been an appealing, nomadic kind of existence, without any real cares. At least, none that really mattered until her father had met that girl!

Lula—even now Liza could scarcely bear to think of her name. It had too foreign a ring, or so she tried to persuade herself, having stubbornly refused to use it in the diaries which she had filled so desperately, but had never been able to look at since she had left the island. Since Dan died.

She could see now that for a man of barely fifty to become infatuated with a girl of thirty was far from incredible. It had been her father's apparent violation of his own strict code of conduct that she had found hard to take. The girl, until Liza and Dan had arrived, had apparently been happily married, although her husband had been working hundreds of miles away and not been home for months. If it hadn't been for the baby Liza might have forgiven them. Liza could still wince visibly when she thought of it, as remorse struck painfully. She must have been a little out of her mind to have made such a fuss, but at her age, a very young nineteen, it hadn't been too easy to see clearly.

'You ought to have had more sense than to be late this morning;' Chloe had hissed as Liza, still faintly breathless, had emerged from the cloakroom after ensuring she was neat enough not to arouse Miss Russell's wrath again.

'Why particularly this morning?' Liza had hissed back in a hoarse whisper, scarcely daring to speak at all, but conscious from the hushed emphasis in Chloe's voice that there was something she ought to know.

'Mrs Latham is expected,' Chloe mouthed, half turning, her smile already fixed to greet an early customer. 'You must be aware of what that means? The red carpet must be out, along with everything else!'

In other words, Liza had supposed as she had hurried to help with the arranging of some new stock, everything, even the atmosphere, must be extra smooth, the sales staff ready to anticipate Mrs Latham's every wish. Such drill might be normal procedure, but in this case, after the last fiasco— whew! There would be lectures about the need for extra effort all around, and Miss Russell would no doubt have already mapped out the necessary itinerary.

Mrs Latham, as everyone knew, was the stepmother of the man who was Lathams. The man who owned, and presumably ran, the huge chain of super-stores of which this was one. Liza had only glimpsed at this great personage once, and although she wisely kept the knowledge to herself, she hadn't cared for what she had seen. It had been shortly after she had first come that he had swept into the department with the lady who was his late father's widow, demanding that she receive an apology from one of the staff who had dared upset Mrs Latham by querying her choice of colour!

When the salesgirl had quivered that she had never intended to offend, his remarks had been nothing short of annihilating, before he had strode off again leaving the poor girl in tears behind him. Liza had been surprised that Miss Russell hadn't protested, but if she had done so might it not have brought Grant Latham's wrath down on her own head?

Later Liza had heard her murmuring to the head sales-girl that Mr Grant usually lost his patience when his step-mother was around and had to take it out on someone. Nothing that had happened was of any real consequence. It had merely been a small demonstration of a man's desire to placate a rather difficult woman in order to be rid of her as quickly as possible. Mrs Latham, fortunately, did not come up to town very often.

Which, while it might have been true, surely did not justify such unfairness? After all, he must have known the girl hadn't dared answer back. Yet Liza had wondered if she could have stood meekly and taken all he had to say without retaliating.

But that had all been several months ago, and now she could barely remember what he looked like. At the time, from a sort of self-defensive position half hidden behind a rail of evening gowns, it hadn't really been possible to get a good look. All she seemed to recall was a kind of dark, prowling elegance, combined with a hard, unprepossessing manner that hadn't appealed to her one bit.

Of course she was not unaware of the gossip that circu-lated the store from time to time about a man of his age and position who, surprisingly it seemed, remained unmarried. It was also whispered he was something of a genius, a man who had built up a virtual empire from very little. But what appeared to interest the staff most was his known popu-larity with women. Not everything that filtered through could be true, Liza realised, but she saw no reason to doubt that there must be a modicum of truth in at least some of it. She had heard it said he had a brother. Surely there couldn't be two of them!

Mrs Latham had arrived about eleven o'clock, and though Grant Latham came with her he obviously didn't intend to stay while she replenished her wardrobe. She would be quite safe, he was heard to state, in the capable hands of Miss Russell.

Liza, who unfortunately happened to be standing nearby

as they came into the department, couldn't avoid over-hearing Mrs Latham ask eagerly, 'Couldn't you wait for me, Grant? You know how I value your opinion.'

'Not a chance, Paula, I'm afraid,' he had refused abruptly, and Liza had been horrified to see what seemed suspiciously like tears spring to the woman's eyes.

Mrs Latham was smart. Around sixty, Liza guessed, and obviously highly strung. Certainly in need of the reassurance her stepson was so reluctant to give. He must be a brute! Remembering his last momentous appearance, Liza was convinced of it, and recklessly she had allowed her indignation to show.

It was only as she had looked away from Mrs Latham's unhappy face that she had met a pair of icy blue eyes and become momentarily frozen, the flush which had subsequently stained her smooth cheeks red-hot by comparison. Liza hadn't realised that her disdainful expression had been painted so vividly across her face as to make the reading of it unmistakable!

Smoothly Grant Latham had halted in his tracks, no mean artist, it seemed, in the gentle art of manoeuvre as he had continued to comment lightly to a riveted Miss Russell, who had tactfully passed his stepmother on to the head salesgirl. And all the while he talked he had managed to keep his dark gaze narrowly fixed over her head on a now totally embarrassed Liza!

If that had been the worst of it, it would have been bad enough, but she'd been aghast at what he had said as Mrs Latham had disappeared into a cubicle. 'You have quite a reputation for the excellence of your staff, Miss Russell, no doubt owing to your careful vigilance. Could this be slipping?' His voice had seemed full of deliberately intentional emphasis.

'I'm sorry, Mr Grant, I'm afraid I don't understand?' Miss Russell's face had registered only shocked disbelief.

'That girl over there,' neatly he stepped around a bewildered Miss Russell, and advanced purposefully on a shaking Liza. 'This girl,' he said, quite clearly and coldly, as Miss Russell caught up with him anxiously. 'I don't recall seeing her before?'

Liza, other than as a degenerate object, might not have existed!

'Miss Dean has been with us since spring,' Miss Russell, still wholly confused, frowned suspiciously. 'Is she—I mean, has she . . .?'

Grant Latham shrugged his broad shoulders, the taunting note in his voice surprisingly like an insult. 'It was merely her expression that didn't seem quite right.' As Liza had almost visibly squirmed, he added, with apparent generosity, 'But perhaps it was simply the way I happened to glance at her.'

Apprehension had rippled over Liza, and some small instinct within had urged her swiftly to apologise. Yet beneath his coolly derisive stare her voice had curiously deserted her. She could only stand in mutinous silence when, as if intent on punishing her for hidden crimes, his dark blue glance slid contemplatively over her, lingering narrowly on her long shining hair, the supple, sensuous curves of her slender figure before returning to study the wide defiance of her thickly fringed eyes.

'I'm sure I must have been mistaken,' he suggested again, as Liza stiffened, remaining obstinately mute. 'Possibly you would agree, Miss Dean, but I begin to wonder if you are usually so deliberately dumb?'

Miss Russell, clearly aware by now of Liza's sullen expression if unable to account for it, did the apologising for her. 'Miss Dean was late in getting in this morning, sir. No doubt this has distracted her a little, as she is usually a very good girl.'

'Is she now?' His eyes had glinted, a tiny flicker of diabolical amusement. 'I am aware that she appears to have distinct possibilities. A little more discipline, perhaps?'

Inwardly Liza had seethed. They might have been discussing a new machine, without the ability to understand one word that was being said about it! Yet unable to withstand Grant Latham's vivid blue appraisal, she lowered her head, her limbs, for no reason she could think of, quivering.

His whole manner, his looks, were way beyond her. Far beyond the comprehension of her own limited experience, she suspected. And, knowing this, as he undoubtedly had, he had intentionally set out to humiliate her for what could only have been a very minor, human transgression, and she vowed she would never forgive him. Why should the so high stoop so low? she wondered bitterly, her expression more revealing than she knew as she battled silently with an intense degree of unfamiliar emotions.

So incensed was she that she scarcely heard the half of Miss Russell's subsequent lecture that seemed to go on long after he had gone. Eventually reaching the closing stages, Miss Russell, apparently satisfied that Liza had been suitably chastised, concluded rather less severely, 'One's expression must always be closely guarded, my dear, especially when customers are around. To find a salesgirl positively glaring when one enters a department is very off-putting, to say the least! And you mustn't think Mr Latham unfair. His sharpness for detail has helped put him where he is today. It has probably become a habit but, my goodness, where would we be without him!'

I can't think, and I'm frankly not interested, Liza felt like retorting sharply, and while she bit her lip to stop such unwise words escaping was unaware that once again her expressively sensitive face was speaking them for her.

Miss Russell, her eyes as keen as her employer's, noticed immediately, and suddenly infuriated, she sprang to her feet. 'Apparently, Miss Dean,' she cried, 'words have no effect! You can work through your lunch hour, and don't start quoting rules and regulations to me! Remember you are still a trainee and, as such, have a lot to learn. Just be thankful Mr Latham didn't ask for your instant dismissal!'

'I say, Dean, I am sorry,' Chloe sympathised brightly on her way to the canteen. 'Russell can be an old bitch when she thinks she has reason. Still, while you're tidying up the cubicles you can always practise this smile she's so keen about.'

Liza managed a wry shrug, yet loyalty towards the militant Miss Russell stirred surprisingly. 'It was completely my own fault,' she admitted frankly.

'Such honesty,' Chloe giggled, glancing swiftly over her shoulder before adding in a furtive whisper, 'It must have been worth it to get such a close-up of you know who! What wouldn't I give for the same opportunity!'

'I just wish you would shut up, Chloe,' Liza said tonelessly. 'After all, if I'd owned a shop and caught one of my assistants glaring at me . . .'

'I wouldn't imagine for a moment it could have anything to do with me,' Chloe mimicked superlatively before tacking on wryly, 'Actually I think Mrs Latham is at fault. I mean, why doesn't she just pop in here quietly by herself? It's whispered that she goes to his office and literally drags him out, and he's so irritated that he's actually on the lookout for a scapegoat.'

'So I've heard.' Liza shifted uncomfortably, apprehensive that someone might hear them discussing the Lathams like this and not keen to incur Miss Russell's wrath again. Not three times on the same day!

Yet Chloe might have a point. In spite of her former sympathy, Liza had seen that Mrs Latham could be a tedious sort of woman. A fine dance she had led them that morning before pronouncing herself satisfied. She had almost turned the department upside down and then bought only one gown! No man could probably be expected to put up with that!

'Still . . .' Chloe was meditating wistfully, as if following Liza's line of thought, 'he is a bit of a dream, and if it wasn't for that rather trying stepmamma of his we might never see him. And even to view from a distance is better than not at all! I'll see you're sent a nice sandwich, Dean, so bear up.'

Quite naturally Liza seemed to have lost what little appetite she had got, along with any ability to concentrate clearly on what she was doing. Mechanically she began tidying the cluttered cubicle Mrs Latham had left behind, seeing not the piles of discarded clothes and hat-boxes but a pair of glinting, midnight-blue eyes, which had reminded her illogically of dark tropical skies before a storm. Eyes which had so swiftly summed her up, looked right through her, discarded her of any consequence!

Rather blindly she gathered up an armful of gossamer chiffon. Mrs Latham had refused to let anything be put back on the rails until she had finally decided. He was about thirty-six, someone had said. With all that vitality he could be ageless. Really, Chloe ought to be more careful— such mountains of tissue from the hat-boxes! There was something about him, apart from his good looks which, of course, were undeniable. Miss Russell would have a fit if she could see this little lot! Fortunately she had rushed straight off to lunch after seeing Mrs Latham off.

Liza paused, frowning. It couldn't matter that she hadn't liked him when so many others obviously did! Besides, who was she to even dare think about it?

It was then, in the middle of this muddled, somewhat heart-shaking introspection, that Liza first smelt burning. To begin with it was only faint, like the lingering aroma of cigarette smoke, and she remembered that Mrs Latham had been smoking. At least, not much. Liza had seen her light one. To help her make up her mind, she had said. Lulled for a second as she recalled this, Liza relaxed. Then suddenly, to her horror, the whole cubicle appeared to burst into flames, a wild panorama of leaping colour that swept greedily through the lengths of gauzy material. Like some sleeping monster which had suddenly sprung to life, it devoured and gathered strength. She would never have believed it if she hadn't seen it with her own eyes!

Panic-stricken for a moment, Liza strove desperately to keep her head, even while terror mounted wildly within her. She was well aware of the usual procedure in such emergencies, but all she could think of was that this was almost the top floor and that fire, once it had a good hold, could be a dreadful hazard, even considering the help of modern appliances. Liza did in fact in those first moments call for help, but perhaps because of the enclosed cubicle and the lunch hour, no one heard her, as no one came.

She saw instantly that it had started in one corner where the flames burnt fiercely behind a pile of tissue, and, without being entirely conscious of what she was doing, she clutched the pile of clothes she was holding tightly in her hands and began beating at the flames in an attempt to put them out. Which surely should not be impossible as the fire had only just started, but a terrible anxiety drove her furiously on in case she should fail. As she had failed before to do the right thing, and perhaps because of it, her father had died?

Afterwards Liza was told that what she had tried to do, what she had in fact succeeded in doing, had been almost impossible. She had acted very foolishly indeed and could easily have lost her life if it hadn't been that an unusually benevolent fate had apparently decreed that she deserved not to. By the time she was discovered she had managed to put out most of the fire, so that all there remained for the fire brigade to do was to deal with the heap of smouldering embers.

The assistant who found her had received an awful fright. There had been smoke escaping from the closed cubicle, and when she thrust open the door, she had found Liza standing, staring down at her scorched hands, a look of extreme shock on her face, seemingly not aware of what she was doing. Liza's clothing had been blackened and burnt, her hair singed and covered with fragments of sooty cloth, and the horrified woman had just failed to catch her before she fell in a dead faint, hitting her head as she did so with a resounding crack against the edge of the open door.

Liza was in hospital almost three weeks; during the first two, heavily sedated because of her burns. She was aware of people coming and going, of nurses tending her, but only vaguely, like shadows in a world of dreams. It wasn't unpleasant simply to lie there, wrapped in a drowsy cocoon of unreality which nothing from the past seemed able to penetrate.

Even when she did become fully conscious of her surroundings she found she could not recall anything of her life before she had come here, something which she was told should not be allowed to depress her. It wasn't unusual for shock, together with a blow on the head, to cause a temporary loss of memory. There was nothing to be alarmed about, all she must do was concentrate on being as patient as possible. Everything else would fall into place, given time.

All of which, while it was good advice, was very difficult to accept when not even the thin nightgown she was wearing was familiar. They did tell her a little about the incident at the store, of the fire she had so bravely managed to put out, and how everyone praised her. But, although vague pictures filtered through her mind, none of it really made sense, and after a while she was content to leave it. A peculiar exhaustion beset her when she tried too hard, which she found frightening. Yet just to lie and know of nothing but the four white walls around her was the strangest sensation.

Liza didn't so much as recognise Grant Latham when he came, but she did feel inexplicably glad to see him. Later she was sure it must have been his commanding sort of presence which had given her an immediate sense of security, lifting her as it did out of the dark void of despair in which she felt herself to be wallowing. His crisp appearance and looks and manner was straight away something she wanted to cling to, as a swimmer exhausted in deep seas might clutch at a raft, anything that might rescue her from such a perilous situation.

Weakly, as he entered her small room, she shook back her long hair and opened her eyes wide as a curious sensation almost overcame her. She had simply been told that a friend was coming to see her. It had never entered her head that she might have known anyone like this.

Mr Grant Latham, she kept turning his name over in her mind. Exactly how friendly had they been? Did she call him Grant, or Mr Latham? Surely if she'd known him well, she would have remembered? Not even a sick mind could reject a man like this?

But no, there was absolutely nothing, not even a glimmer of anything coming through, although if her mind rejected him, her heart was acting very strangely, racing as if it recognised and reacted to something no other part of her recalled.

As he advanced towards the bed Liza continued to stare at him, her beautiful, translucent green eyes more bewildered than she knew.

He walked right up to the bed and sat down in the chair that the nurse had placed for him, before he spoke, but his manner was easy, as if he had come to visit someone he was very familiar with indeed. 'You're feeling better?' he asked, his voice low, its even timbre very attractive, wholly acceptable, completely soothing to her frayed, taut nerves.

'Yes.' Her own voice, by contrast, was hesitant, and because she was unable to sustain his swiftly searching glance her heavy lashes fluttered on to her pale cheeks. 'That is,' she went on, rather like a painstaking child, 'my hands are still bandaged, but they don't really hurt.'

He pulled his chair nearer and took one of her hands carefully, holding it lightly in his, his wide, rather sensuous mouth tightening grimly. 'That's because you've been sedated. You haven't fully recovered yet, you know.'

The contact of his touch was immediately comforting, frighteningly so; yet Liza had an instinctive feeling that he was holding himself in check, that something about her affected him adversely. In spite of what she had been told, perhaps in some way she had acted foolishly over this fire, and he was having some difficulty in controlling his impatience? She must, she decided as she glanced quickly at him again, try to find out what really happened, anything that might help her to remember.

But her throat was tight, scarcely allowing more than a whisper. 'I'm told I work for you, but they wouldn't say anything more, and I can't remember.'

'Don't try.' His eyes, full of a narrowed intensity, were fixed on her anxious face, and he only answered the last part of her sentence. 'Probably in a few days it will all come back.'

There was no complete reassurance in that! A fretful frown drew her dark, feathery brows together. Why had he come if he didn't intend to help her? When she looked at him she could feel an almost tangible tension mounting within her—a compulsion, and strangely, considering the lethargy that held her, a curious urgency to fight him. Yet she also sensed that she would be crazy to antagonise him.

Wildly her thoughts warred, instinct struggling with common sense, one against the other. Why should she be so torn, so full of confusion? Why did she gain so little comfort from the knowledge that whatever the cost she couldn't let him go? It was utterly bewildering, yet as if seeking to support such a conviction her fingers, seemingly of their own accord, curled convulsively around his and clung tightly.

'There are a few things ...' she began.

'Such as?' he prompted softly, as she hesitated.

'I'm not sure. I feel I'm trying to see through a brick wall. I'm not even sure what it is I want to ask!' It was wholly mortifying that her voice should rise so hysterically, worse that she should suddenly find herself turning to Grant Latham, clinging to him, not merely to his hands but in his arms, where she buried her face against his broad shoulder and wept inconsolably, the need for direct physical contact, for sympathy, so great that nothing else seemed to matter.

She could feel his hands gripping her, no rejection in their touch, holding her ever more closer, letting her distracted tears soak his expensive jacket until he felt the tension slowly ease out of her. It was as if he completely understood her immediate need to disperse the terrifying sensation of total isolation that consumed her, and was willing to help in any way he could. He allowed her to cry and listened to her incoherent mutterings, his fingers threading through her bright, tumbled hair, gently massaging the bare skin of her nape and shoulders, his arm soothingly around her trembling body. Slowly his head bent, his lips lightly touching her damp cheek, his expression grimly compassionate if oddly curious, containing as it did an element of surprise that he should find himself so naturally in such a position.

'Liza ...'

From a distance his voice came very softly, and she felt the movement of his mouth against her ear. 'You can trust me, Liza. Everything will be all right, I do assure you.'

He didn't ask her to pull herself together, and perhaps for this reason she tried to, although she was content, as the tears dried on her flushed cheeks, to remain where she was, caught up in the safe circle of his arms. She sighed and tried to nod as he continued to murmur soothingly, for the first time in days feeling at peace. A few minutes ago she had been wondering about him, thinking he would never be her kind of person. Now he seemed as much a part of her as her right hand.

In his arms she felt herself coming miraculously alive. Nothing exactly traumatic, but she could feel it amazingly. There was still nothing for her mind to grasp whichever way she turned, but physically she could experience pleasure in the feather light whispering of sensations rioting through her soft, pliant body. Which must prove she was at least partly capable of all the normal reactions?

Or was this normal, the positive tongues of flame which began to lick through her under the sympathetic administrations of Grant's hands? Had she known this peculiar rapture before? An astringent flare of impatience smote her because the answer eluded her, and she drew back so she could see his face.

'Grant,' she breathed, her breath faint on his cheek, her eyes dazed, 'how well did I know you?'

'Well enough.' For the first time he smiled, faintly, as if gratified to see her returning colour, though his eyes were guarded. 'Haven't I just told you, you must trust me?'

'Yes, of course...' Because for no apparent reason she found his reply far from satisfying, Liza's face clouded, and as if he understood the perplexities which beset her, he dropped a swiftly caressing kiss on her soft mouth before laying her gently back again on to her pillows. 'You wouldn't want to have me thrown out?' he teased lightly.

'No!' It was just one word, but she uttered it fervently, convinced that he was reluctant to let her go. He watched her consideringly, and she remained quite still where he had laid her for another minute before she spoke.

'No one has told me anything about how I came to be burnt. I can only remember vaguely and I haven't had any other visitors.'

'And this worries you, of course.' His eyes went broodingly over her and her whole body went taut, recalling those inexplicable moments in his arms.

'Please, Grant,' she pleaded, feeling so much nearer to him that it was easier to beg.

'It doesn't frighten you?' he queried cautiously.

'Oh, please,' she whispered, her hand half extended to clutch his again, but she brought it quickly back to her side as she sensed a certain withdrawal. Only her eyes remained on his beseechingly, reflecting how his rejection hurt. 'You see, I don't know how a case of lost memory is normally treated. I suppose there is a sort of normal procedure, but surely it could do no harm if someone like you were to furnish a few details. About the fire, I mean. Details the nursing staff couldn't possibly know and which might help.'

Grant Latham said abruptly, 'Well, already you appear to know that there was a fire in my shop where you work, and you put it out. With your bare hands, hence the burns. What you probably don't know is that my stepmother was perhaps indirectly responsible.'

Liza stared at him, her bewildered face a perfect mirror for her thoughts. She didn't even remember Grant's stepmother! 'How could she be—responsible?' she whispered.

His mouth thinned. 'She had been smoking. Perhaps she failed to put out her cigarette properly.'

'You can't be sure!'

'One scarcely ever can be in a case like this.' His voice was even but his eyes too cold. 'At least she didn't try to deny it completely, but she declares she put it out before she put it down somewhere. It could have smouldered, as there seems nothing else to account for such a fire.'

Unhappily Liza stirred, sensing that Grant regretted having to make such a disclosure, but not altogether for obvious reasons! Nervously she stared at him. If, as he said, it was his stepmother's fault, then he could be finding a sense of responsibility irksome. 'You don't have to let it trouble you on my account,' she said starkly.

'Naturally it does,' he returned crisply, but she could see his manner was cooling by the minute, as though it was only by great effort he remained patient. 'Don't you see,' he went on, 'that to go into the immediate details of the fire isn't going to help you? You'll only be agitated. Isn't it sufficient to know that you put the fire out and consequently are something of a heroine? But everything will work out all right. You'll be well taken care of.'

'I'm sorry,' she whispered stiffly, feeling suddenly near to tears again at the curtness of his tones. 'I'm sure I must have some relations who'll be willing to take me off your hands. There must be someone?' she cried with a new urgency, when he made no reply.

'You can't think of anyone?' he glanced at her sharply, his mouth hard and firm, but compassion returned once more to his face at the unconscious pathos in her tones.

'No—at least,' bewildered, she blinked, 'I hadn't thought about any such thing until now.'

He said carefully, watching her closely, cautious as to how far he could go, 'You've mentioned at the shop that your parents are both dead, but I believe they died some time ago. You've been living on your own, so this is probably correct.'

'Oh.' Liza waited for the pain of shock, but nothing came. It was as if the news had no meaning. 'Anyway, thank you for telling me.' She paused. 'Where exactly do I live, do you know?'

His voice was edgy, seeming to imply that there was something he disliked. 'You have a bed-sitter, if it helps you to get the general picture.'

'I see.' She had forgotten that she had asked where, and not noticed that once again he evaded a direct answer. Staring down at her bandaged hands, she was instantly diverted.

'My hands should soon heal,' she said, 'then I shall be able to return to work. I'm almost sure to recognise the other girls and possibly everything will come back. Then I won't need to pester you with any more questions, Mr Latham,' she finished ruefully.

'Stop it,' his words were hard and brief, 'and call me Grant.'

'Did I—ever?' Just to look at him, so tall and dark with a kind of arrogant, remote vitality, made such a notion seem indescribably foolish. Instinctively Liza knew, in spite of a vague, half-formed longing that it should be otherwise, that never in a thousand years could she have achieved any degree of familiarity with a man like this! And yet...

The impatience in his abrupt exclamation evaded her, as his eyes ran over her to take in all her young, mixed-up uncertainty. His hand went out to drop lightly on her arm, stilling immediately the fine fever of her barely suppressed agitation, if indirectly raising one of a different kind.

'You have no idea just how things were between us, Liza, the exact stage of our relationship. One day I might tell you, but not now. Right now you must concentrate on getting better, and rest. I was only allowed in here on the promise that I would do nothing to upset you, and didn't stay too long. So if you want to see me again tomorrow——'

Was that a promise or a threat? Grant gave her no time to decide as, after a slight, reassuring increase of pressure, he removed his hand from her arm and rose to his feet, replacing his chair where he had found it. But for a moment before he left he returned to the bed and stared down at her, his mouth strangely compressed, as if her unconscious fragility, her undoubted beauty, the lost look in the wide green eyes affected him more than he cared to admit.

Yet his farewell was brief, giving nothing away. 'Goodnight, Liza Dean,' he said soberly. 'Sleep well, and try not to worry. You won't get rid of me as easily as all that.'

CHAPTER TWO

IT was another week before Liza was allowed out of hospital, and during that week Grant Latham came to see her each day. As no one else came she looked eagerly forward to seeing him, and spent most of the time between his visits trying fiercely to recall his shop, the kind of premises he would have, the sort of people who worked there. It couldn't be so very large, she decided, if he knew all his workers personally, as he knew her. Somehow the idea of a small, cosy establishment pleased her enormously. It would be more or less a family affair, which probably explained why none of the other staff had time to come and see her. In a small business the absence of even one person could mean the others having to help out. They would be working longer hours and be too busy and tired of an evening to visit the hospital, but no doubt Grant would give them all the news.

So much did she think about this shop that occasionally she received a faint picture, as if she was hovering on the very verge of a momentous discovery, then everything would fade and she would be left with the usual frightening blank wall. Her mind, Liza concluded unhappily, was exactly like the television set in her room when it had developed a fault and, try as she might, the night nurse could not get a clear picture. Just the odd flash, a distorted blur that no one understood.

Liza was filled with an ever-increasing sense of frustration, a near-panic which she tried to control, but which showed itself in many obvious ways. Daily she grew paler, filled with a tense, overbearing sadness as the terrifying

23

feeling of isolation increased. A deep depression gnawed at her, shadowing her lovely, clear-cut face, scarcely allowing her to relax. The only time she felt the awful rigidness fall from her was when Grant was around, but much as she was coming to depend on him there was still, where he was concerned, a hint of reservation. Inexplicable, perhaps, but definitely there. Some things she still couldn't tell him. He so obviously felt responsible for her accident that if she were to confess how much she relied on him, he might only feel trapped!

The hospital psychiatrist saw her regularly, and her doctors had been extremely kind, talking to her frequently. It all seemed so simple on the face of it. The psychiatrist said that her loss of memory need not necessarily be directly because of the fire. That something in her past could be responsible for her amnesia, something which she might have been desperately trying to forget but had not succeeded in doing so. The shock caused by this second accident could be merely providing a sort of cover-up for another which in some way had been extremely significant.

Which didn't seem to be much help, not even appearing logical to a Liza who couldn't remember anything of even one accident. It seemed crazy to talk of two—especially something that had happened long ago.

Of her past she didn't even get the blurred impressions which sometimes came through of the shop. Not that she didn't appreciate all that was being done for her, but much of it only seemed to fill her with a greater confusion. As her hands healed and, physically at any rate, she recovered, she grew very anxious to be out of hospital, to go to some place of her own, however small. If she could find something to do, to keep herself busy, might she not eventually escape the blank spaces of her mind which so filled her with apprehension? Yet contrarily, at times, the thought of returning to an empty flat alarmed her almost as much.

Life seemed to have taken on the proportions of a giant jigsaw puzzle, and even a lot in her immediate circumstances perplexed her. She appeared to possess a large wardrobe of the most decoratively expensive nightwear which was envied, if discreetly, by the entire nursing staff. No one ever mentioned where they had come from, but surely a girl who worked for her living as a shop assistant couldn't afford such luxury?

Uneasily she glanced down at the fragile, silky negligée she wore now. Making a great pretence of being amused, she had asked one of her younger nurses how much must she have paid for it, and the girl had laughed and replied, at least a month's salary!

'But how could I spare that much?' Unconsciously, Liza had expressed her bewildered doubts aloud.

'You ought to stop worrying,' the young nurse had smiled, 'and take what the good Lord provides.'

Which was all very well, Liza had pondered fretfully, but she doubted if the Lord, however good, had anything to do with this!

Her room, too, was another thing that kept her vaguely worried. It was a room in the private wing, something which she had discovered quite by accident. Two of the staff had been whispering outside her door, when they had apparently thought her asleep. 'One of the best,' they had said. 'Nothing too good!' They had sounded unduly impressed.

The next day she had tackled Grant about it, but he had been as evasive as everyone else, and looked immediately impatient, as he always did, when pressed for a direct answer. He had muttered something about the National Health, taking obvious comfort from the fact that she had no idea what he was talking about. Nor had he stopped to explain.

Liza was naturally not without some common sense, and suspected that he was supplying a lot more than he would ever admit to. If only she knew for sure! If only there could be some way of repaying him. This way, it seemed, he intended depriving her of even the pleasure of saying thank you. Still, one day he might be prepared to listen.

In the meanwhile she strove not to antagonise him, as she was beginning to realise he was coming to be a kind of vital necessity; that she watched for his arrival all day, and was

thrown into a positive panic of despair if he was more than
a few minutes late. And while something about him disturbed her profoundly, it was something she seemed unable
to do without. The habit of confiding in him was growing.
He was someone to whom she could speak of her mounting
bewilderment.

When he walked in that evening he brought chocolates
and magazines, together with a huge bunch of autumn
flowers. 'From the flower stall at the end of the road,' he
said lightly, 'although I do have a garden.'

'A garden?' Her lips moved with a pleasure she could
almost feel as, tearfully delighted, she buried her face in the
rich fragrance of the yellow blooms. Suddenly, without
doubt, she knew she loved flowers; that somewhere, at some
time, she had been used to having them around. But as
always when her memory jerked, there was also a flash of
pain, and, exquisite as the flowers were, she instantly rejected them, thrusting them from her, back into the hands
of the man who stood watching her closely. 'You must give
them to the nurse,' she said quickly, 'right away. They must
need water.'

'No great urgency,' Grant replied, still lightly, while his
glance remained keen on her suddenly taut face. 'Don't you
like them?' he asked abruptly, as he placed them apparently carelessly on the table over her bed.

'Yes, yes, of course!' But the pain still moved through
her and she didn't even want to look at them. She wished he
had put them somewhere else.

Usually, she knew, he was willing to let her small eva-
sions pass, but this time it seemed he was bent on a little
experiment. His mouth tightened with a hint of the determination she was coming to recognise.

'When I gave you those flowers, you remembered something, didn't you?'

'I'm not sure.' The pale silk of her extravagantly lacy
nightdress moved slightly with the agitation of her small
breasts. 'It hurts if I do,' she confessed, her eyes downcast,
as if a little ashamed of such an admission while unable to
withhold it.

Usually, at the first signs of distress Grant tried sympathetically to distract her, to such an extent that, childlike, she was coming to rely on it when anything upset her. It appeared he wasn't willing to let her get away with this any longer. Startled, she felt his weight heavy against her as, ignoring the waiting chair, he sank down on the edge of the bed, his fingers sliding beneath her drooping chin and lifting it firmly so that he might see her face properly. 'You can't run away from reality for ever, you know.'

The feel of his hand on her bare skin stung almost more than the shock she had just received, and Liza tried to take refuge in anger. 'You brought those flowers deliberately, didn't you?' she cried.

'You could say.'

'You're not the sort of man to go carrying round bunches of flowers. You would get your secretary to ring, and it would be something exotic, like an orchid . . .'

'For a girl who's supposed to have lost her memory you seem remarkably clued up.' His voice was curtly derisive, and she almost collapsed from the unfamiliar hardness.

She could see herself reflected in the darkness of his narrowed eyes, and flinched as if he had hit her. 'You have to give me time. They say I need it.'

'Something I don't.'

She could barely make out the words he had muttered beneath his breath. His dry expression seemed to force her to go on. 'You surely don't think I'm simply pretending . . .?' Despairingly, her voice trailed off.

'No. I'm being too impatient.' He studied her face intently, the colour that came and went under her exquisite skin. So close, as he tried and failed to find a single flaw. Coolly deliberate, his other hand came up, pushing the heavy, tumbled hair back from her forehead, tracing gently the line of her smooth winged brows. 'Incredible,' he said softly, as his eyes and fingers explored.

And because waves of tension began to hit her, the same as she recalled when he had held her before, she struggled back from his grasp, murmuring incoherently, 'They seem to imagine it could be something in my past!'

Something flickered in Grant's eyes for a second as he abruptly let her go, before it was replaced by his usual inscrutable self. Yet there was a moment's frowning silence before he spoke. 'Can't you remember anything? Your father's death, perhaps, or a boy-friend?'

Her breath caught, hurting. She could understand death being a shock – in some circumstances, but this other that Grant mentioned? 'How could a boy-friend...?' she stumbled, staring at him uncertainly.

'An affair,' he supplied briefly, as if driving himself with hard deliberation. 'Something of this kind can be pretty devastating to some people.'

Liza felt herself flushing and she hoped he didn't think it was with guilt. 'No,' she said, trying to speak evenly and frankly so that he wouldn't think she was completely naïve, 'I can't recall anything like that. But even if I could, is it—I mean could it be...'

'Be what?' Impatient again, he cut sharply through her confused sentence, his eyes, full of the suspicion she had hoped to avoid, on her hot cheeks.

'Devastating enough to affect one's mind?' she echoed his astringent tone, or tried to.

'Possibly.' His mouth thinned as he noted the anxiety behind the coolness of her voice. 'But you must remember that it's not your mind which is affected, merely your memory, which is quite another thing.' Fractionally he paused before adding, 'To return to the boy-friend angle, it could be something to think about. You can't be sure.'

'I don't know why, but I feel I can be. Why do you insist?'

'Such emphasis,' he mocked gently. 'Better put it down to curiosity. Aren't you ever curious about me?'

'No—that is...' Liza had been about to deny it hotly, and this time her flush was guilty as she quickly changed her mind. She was curious! It had occurred to her that he could be married, but she doubted somehow that he had a wife. No married man would surely have either the time or inclination to sit by a girl's bedside each evening, even if he did so impersonally, because she was one of his employees.

But he could have had affairs, not innocent ones either, by the look of him! His dark good looks were of the unforgettable kind, and probably enabled him to pick and choose where women were concerned. He seemed very much of a man, with a man's needs . . .

At this thought there came again the sudden pain, and a small frightened gasp escaped Liza as her face went white. As if, this time, something really terrible had stabbed her—some naked truth that could be the real heart of the matter, but which she could never, never face!

'Liza!' Grant's voice came, hard and inflexible, like a man nearing the end of his tolerance. 'What is it?' Firmly he grasped her shoulders, something he seemed to be doing more frequently. 'You've got to stop tearing yourself apart like this. When I asked that stupid question I had no intention of upsetting you.'

Momentarily she let her bright head droop against him, not knowing how to reply, unconsciously trembling while she sought to hide her conflicting emotions with a lightly teasing shrug. 'Perhaps it was the thought of your affairs that upset me,' she confessed with a faint smile, thinking that it must be very near the truth.

'Oh, Liza,' his hands tightened ruefully, 'I've had relationships with women, but for a man of my age it shouldn't surprise you, my dear. Not enough to make you tremble like this.'

'Well, it was something.' Nervously she bit at her full lower lip. 'How would I really know? Perhaps I'm coming to rely on you too much—it could be a mistake. Anyway, I'm sorry. I didn't mean to pry into your love-life.'

'Liza!' His teeth glinted white, as his hand caressed her burnished hair. 'How innocently you put it. You're too much of a babe to be delving into matters like that. My love-life, as you so quaintly put it, is practically non-existent. To a man love is not always the basic requirement.'

Was he trying to shock her further? There was a hint of something in his enigmatic expression that made her suspect that he was trying, if gently, to shake her sluggish memory. Yet his hands on her hair and shoulders were tolerant, as if nothing was of any great consequence and there was all the time in the world.

Because she didn't know how to answer him, if indeed he expected any reply to his frankly brutal statement, Liza tried to say calmly, 'I suppose you know best. Sometimes I find myself talking a lot of nonsense without meaning to. You see, every now and again I get the most peculiar feelings of something coming through, but it always recedes again, as it did when you gave me those flowers.'

He half lifted her and pushed her back against her pillows, holding her captive merely with his eyes. 'You're too sensitive,' he said crisply. 'You could be reacting to the present more than the past, and you shouldn't be having to contend with two things at a time like this. Maybe if you learnt to accept me without question, to leave it at that for a while.'

She ran a nervous hand behind her nape, shaking out her long hair to ease a sudden tension. 'How do you mean?'

'Some part of you is fighting me, or unconsciously resisting what I stand for.'

'Which is?'

'A new experience, I believe—one you've never had to cope with before. You're over-reacting. Your pulse races each time I come near you.'

'And you don't approve?' Her green eyes clouded, acknowledging some truth in what he was trying to explain, but not convinced that it was exactly as he said. It could simply be a trick of the imagination. He didn't disturb her to any uncomfortable degree, in fact she liked it when he held her lightly, and his voice could be wonderfully soothing. It was only when the pressure increased, when his arms tightened, that something hit her, stiffening a slipping resistance against a new, inexplicable emotion which her body seemed more willing to accept than her mind.

So—Grant could be right, but to herself her incomprehensible yearnings made no sense whatsoever. Unless it made her guilty of a degree of procrastination? She thought of Grant Latham perhaps too much, when it might profit her more to concentrate every spare minute on unravelling her too evasive past?

The soft sigh that escaped her trembled wistfully on her lips. If only he wasn't so attractive! Her glance lingered on the deep, determined cleft of his hard chin before she raised her eyes to his, intensely expressive. He hadn't attempted to answer her short query, but she saw that his eyes were brilliant with restrictive thoughts behind the narrowed lids.

Her breath drew quickly. When he stared at her like that he seemed very familiar; someone she had known all her life, if she couldn't remember anything else! The degree of familiarity was almost frightening, an alarming, unknown element, something to match the confusingly blank spaces of her mind, and, unconsciously terrified, she shrank from him.

'You see, Liza,' Grant's laugh was swift and hard as he unerringly totalled up the sum of her blank despair, 'you must undoubtedly put me to one side until you can take it.'

Did he have to be so ambiguous? She was, after all, nearly twenty—something more than a child! Yet occasionally she felt like one, unable to challenge in any way the ruthless logic of his arguments. Flushing miserably, she searched rather desperately for a few sophisticated words which might impress him, or at least shake his sardonic ego, but none came. Instead, she heard herself pleading meekly, 'I think if I were out of here, leading a normal life, I should soon be well.'

He appeared to relax fractionally, yet his voice was cautious. 'It could be too soon. How do you really feel? Your hands?'

'They're healing, as you can see.' She turned the scarred palms uppermost. 'It's just a matter of time.'

Sharply he frowned, as if the still red, wrinkled skin on her slim fingers was abhorrent to him. 'Yes,' he said tightly, 'I'm aware of that. You could be right.'

Liza guessed he had spoken to someone in authority. Daily, she had been told, he kept a check on her progress. It surprised her, the trouble he took when he must have enough to do in his own business. But if this was a private room it must be costing him a lot, and there was small doubt in her mind as to who was paying for it! More than Grant could probably afford, and she couldn't possibly let it continue any longer. It was up to her to make a definite move.

'I really don't think they can do much more for me,' she asserted in firmer tones, as, curiously indecisive for once, he rose and wandered restlessly to the window.

But without looking out he swung round, apparently finding it necessary to satisfy himself on one or two points. 'Aren't you comfortable here?'

She blinked before what seemed an all-out attack, and hurried to waylay any impression that she was ungrateful. 'Oh, yes, certainly! Everyone has been extremely kind. In fact,' she hesitated, smiling nervously, 'I could have dreamt it, but sometimes I've had the distinct impression I've been treated like a VIP. But now I would like to go home.'

'Home?'

Why did he sound so sceptical? Her eyes widened. Where else did he think she could go? Naturally he would imagine she couldn't manage, and again she stirred restlessly against the impression that he felt responsible for her accident and felt it irksome. 'Once I'm home,' she managed to smile brightly, 'I'll soon recover completely, you'll see.'

Grant rounded on her, so swiftly that momentarily she felt dizzy as his eyes took in every inch of her, not obviously reassured by what he could see. 'Only if you had someone to look after you properly, which you haven't, not there. You must be mad even to think of it! You couldn't even find your way around until your memory comes back.'

She flushed. Must he remind her so curtly? She knew well her own limitations, but people had surely managed with worse, and if she didn't get out of here quickly she would never be able to repay him. Already the size of her debt was causing too many fraught moments! It wasn't original, but she felt compelled to repeat stubbornly, 'I'm going!'

His eyes caught her small, mutinous expression, the

dampness of a despairing perspiration on her pale brow. It was obvious that he guessed she was in no fit condition to fight him, while in no way prepared to change her mind.

'Okay,' he agreed briefly, but added firmly, with the rather frightening authority she was becoming used to, 'I'll see what can be arranged. Just as long as you leave everything to me, I promise you won't have to stay here any longer than necessary.'

They said she could leave at the end of the week, and Liza was surprised that it had, after all, been so easy. At one time she had thought she might have to remain for months, imprisoned in the huge hospital block like a prisoner in a cell. A word from Grant Latham had worked wonders! A man of his calibre, of course, could do just that, or so it seemed to Liza. So pleased was she by the news that she could have denied him nothing, least of all a few charitable thoughts.

Exactly at this point Liza stopped, not allowing herself to consider that once away from the hospital she might not see much of him any more. He had promised to see to everything, but there must be limits to anyone's generosity. To imagine he had grown almost as necessary as food and drink could only be absurd. The ridiculous wanderings of a confused, inconsistent mind!

It was simply that she was well enough, or they would never have let her go. However, she wasn't so pleased when the chief nursing officer remarked firmly,

'You are far from completely recovered yet, my dear. You will need to return for treatment, but Mr Latham will take care of all that.'

How much longer could Grant be expected to go on doing this. She must be at fault herself in seeming so willing to accept everything he had done for her. Was she not normally a girl of some independence—or had she been used all her life to leaning on someone? Surely not! Somehow she couldn't believe it, the mental picture of such a spineless creature made her shiver with distaste. Yet where would she have been without him? It was difficult to say. But to depend on him too long and too much could become a habit she might, if she wasn't careful, find impossible to break.

She was ready to go now, just waiting for him. The previous evening he had brought her some clothes—new ones, from the shop, he had told her. The ones she had been wearing at the time of the fire were too badly burnt to be of any more use. These were merely replacements of those which she had lost.

Liza had almost gasped when she had slid out of bed, and curiously opened the case after he had gone. She had asked if someone could go to her flat and collect her outdoor things, possibly a dress and cardigan would do. When Grant had said there hadn't been time, she hadn't expected anything like this! The silky underwear, the smart soft blue trouser suit, with its understated shirt, striped in beautifully blended colours which matched perfectly. There was even shoes and a huge swinging shoulder bag with a silver clasp that she immediately loved. Everything appeared to have been chosen with great care, leaving Liza both grateful and thrilled. Dressing that morning had been a pleasure, something to disguise a niggling apprehension of the outside world, which was one thing to be considered from the protective confines of a hospital bed, but quite another when the time actually came to set foot in it!

'Mr Latham is very kind,' she had found herself saying impulsively to the nurse who had helped her to dress. There wasn't a full-length mirror in her room, but what she was able to judge from the small one on the wall and the young nurse's positive gasp of admiration seemed to call for some kind of remark.

'You can say that again!' the nurse exclaimed brightly. 'But I certainly wouldn't mind him even without the kindness. I dare say you could look from here to Land's End and never find another like him.'

Liza blinked. This particular nurse was nice but had always been a shade impulsive. It wasn't the first enthusiastic comment she'd passed about Grant, although the others had been more discreet.

'He's only my boss, you know,' she felt forced to repeat

mildly. 'My own clothes were burnt in the fire at his shop. These are, I suppose, just a few things he's loaned me from stock until I get home.'

'I know all about that too,' the nurse had laughed good-naturedly as she had said goodbye, and left Liza with the distinct impression that she knew a great deal more than she was prepared to say.

Liza's next surprise was Grant's car, a sleek, luxurious vehicle in sparkling white. The upholstery was in leather, superbly soft, and she sank into it as she got in and sat down—not something she had expected a small shopkeeper to own. It was so beautiful that she hardly dared stretch out her legs, but curled them nervously against the seat.

'Relax,' he smiled, as he closed her door firmly and went around the other side. 'You remind me of a small trapped animal, and that was never my intention, you know.'

'It's not you,' she confessed, returning his smile, if somewhat reluctantly, 'I'm afraid I can't be used to such wonderful cars.'

'How do you know?' His voice was smoothly considering. 'You have every appearance of being able to fit in nicely anywhere. I can't think how I haven't noticed you before. You're not the kind of girl I've ever overlooked.'

Liza wanted to tell him that she thought that outrageous, the sort of undefined confession she'd be ashamed to make if she'd been a man! 'I was talking of your car, not the affairs you've had or the ones you have in mind,' she retorted sharply, perhaps indelicately, but certainly with some spirit. Only the faint flush on her cheeks suggested that she was a little astonished at her own temerity.

His grin merely widened. 'Ah, the car! Maybe you think it a trifle extravagant, but I do restrain myself in other directions.'

'Well,' she conceded wryly, 'I suppose you're not married!' It seemed the standard argument of the day, she'd heard a lot of it in the hospital; how the single could afford more. It had seemed to Liza that marriage was often regarded in terms of pounds and pence, that love was the least important part of it.

This time Grant's mouth really did quirk at the corners, as though he found her indescribably amusing. He slid an arm behind her, to fasten her seat belt, something she didn't know about, and, the operation completed, he kept his hand along the back of her seat for a moment. 'You're looking very lovely this evening,' he assured her, 'but a few more remarks like that and you could be in trouble, my dear Liza.'

'I wasn't being curious,' she protested swiftly, 'but I agree, it was a stupid thing to say. Your private life is none of my business,' she added bleakly, not seeing his humour as she kept her pure profile averted, the angle of her chin and mouth an invitation but intensely vulnerable.

'Forget it,' he said abruptly, turning tersely away to switch on the ignition. 'I guess you're feeling too fraught, being just out of hospital and all that, but you don't have to take everything I say too literally. That particular shade of blue suits you. I told Miss Russell it might.'

This spoke of an affinity Liza instantly rejected, a degree of involvement that was beginning to shake her, yet at the same time drawing her magnetically. It seemed imperative that she should know more about him. What she might discover could be wholly shattering, but the handicap of her lost memory was becoming something even more intolerable. 'Who is Miss Russell?' she asked tonelessly.

'You worked under her,' he replied briefly, as if that was a thing of the past. 'Your immediate supervisor, I suppose.'

Liza was grateful that he didn't throw her another narrowed glance. If he frequently tried to prod her memory, occasionally he left her to work it out for herself. He didn't treat her like something on the end of a microscope all the time! 'I don't recall any Miss Russell,' she frowned, then added more eagerly, 'but it does help me to get a sort of general picture. Maybe tomorrow I could go to the store—in fact I must!'

He ignored the excited rise of her young voice as he swung the big car out into the evening traffic. 'Not a hope,' he said laconically. 'Put any such idea out of your head; you have to crawl before you can walk, you know.'

'What do you mean?'

'Just that.'

The even tenor of his voice ruffled her somewhat. Indignantly she glanced at him sideways, 'I can't just sit around waiting for everything to happen. I must try to help myself.'

He laughed, gently mocking. 'And right now you feel capable of anything, but my guess is that long before you're even home you'll feel too exhausted to give the store another thought.'

'It can't be that far!' Her eyes, still fixed on his face, explored his features anxiously before turning quickly to the window. There were only streets and shops, high office buildings, no houses, nothing she recognised. 'How far do we have to go?' she persisted, as he seemed disinclined to answer.

With some impatience she squirmed, hating having to beg and hating him more for making her. 'Grant?' she said.

'Quite a long drive,' he said casually, looking straight ahead, his voice, like his reply, offering no clues. Then, as if he was perfectly aware of her dissatisfaction, he relented. 'You're coming with me this evening, to stay in my house until you've recovered, or at least are much better than you are now.'

Shock froze her, so completely that the sense of chill was almost physical. She shivered convulsively and it showed. 'Grant,' she whispered, uncaring that he knew she was trembling, 'I can't go there. You've done a lot for me and I'm grateful, but . . .'

'Spare me that!' he interposed cuttingly. 'Gratitude is the last thing I want!'

'But don't you see?' It was her turn to cut in, although she couldn't match his eliminating curtness. 'I've nothing else to repay you with, and I refuse to go deeper into your debt, to become a nuisance.'

He jammed on the brakes at a crossing, and Liza's seat belt tightened across her breast as she jerked suddenly forward. 'When you've outstayed your welcome I'll tell you.' He didn't apologise.

'That's beside the point.' Wildly she glanced about her, the need to escape uppermost in her mind. Yet it didn't seem his house she felt so desperate to escape from. There was some blind reluctance within her to face up to another situation that spelled danger. Although of a different kind, it might be no less scorching than the fire she had only just survived.

To her ears, as the car started off again, came the harsh sound of Grant's deeply drawn breath. 'Liza,' he ordered abruptly, 'calm down! No one is going to force you to anything. We've been through all this before and I grow weary. How on earth did you expect to manage in one small third-floor room? Just start and think about it, girl. An elderly landlady, scarcely able to look after herself. No one, and I repeat, no one, would ever hear you if you needed help, and apart from that, can you imagine the isolation there all day on your own?'

'You've done so much!' she protested. 'I don't see how I can allow you to do more.'

He slanted her a swiftly encompassing glance, his gaze touching every bit of her face. 'Debts can often be easier to repay than you imagine, but there's nothing to worry you for a little while yet. Anything I collected from you would be given freely. Whatever else you are, Liza, you can't be a coward, or you would never have stopped to fight that blaze.'

As usual he was too ambiguous, and her mind, which she instinctively felt could be quick, was unable to understand properly the half of what he said. There was merely a lick of fear, some foreboding, but unless it made her uneasy she could conclude nothing else.

The exhaustion Grant spoke of was creeping insidiously over her, the excitement of her release from hospital almost too much. There was a sudden, consuming dizziness, and she wedged herself stiffly against the back of her seat, reluctant that he should guess. Perhaps it would be better to accept the inevitable for the present. She just hadn't the strength left to fight him. What little energy she possessed might be used more sensibly in other ways.

'Where exactly is this house?' she asked carefully, steadying her voice with effort to a normal politeness.

'On the Thames, beside Windsor.'

'Oh . . .' It meant nothing, but it sounded nice.

'It's right on the river.' They were out of the city now, into the suburbs where the driving was easier. Grant appeared to relax slightly, although his glance, continually flicking her, suggested that he kept a wary watch. 'We have private moorings and fishing.'

'I see.' Again this conveyed very little, but he talked as if there were other people. Nervously she pondered, 'You don't live by yourself, then?'

He grinned suddenly. 'Oh no, not that. There's my stepmother, Paula.'

Liza's lips went cold. 'But she's the one with the cigarette,' she faltered. 'She can't possibly want me.'

'On the contrary, she's eager to have you,' his voice came, smoothly convincing. 'You must be generous and allow her the opportunity to make up for the damage she has caused, if inadvertently.'

'That was simply an accident!' Liza swallowed. 'It could happen to anyone and it shouldn't make her feel she owes me anything. Why, she may not even like me!'

'Don't worry,' he retorted soberly, 'she will. The house is mine.'

How did that fit in? In Grant's voice there seemed a hint of hidden threat, directed clearly against the hapless Paula. 'I shouldn't like her to think I'm more or less forcing my way in,' said Liza.

'No, she doesn't think that. She'll be quite kind, if for no other reason than that she doesn't care to have people think badly of her. For heaven's sake relax and stop worrying. If you have a relapse you could find yourself immediately back in hospital.' This time the threat was aimed unmistakably at Liza.

She closed her eyes obediently, with every appearance of following his advice. It was all part of his policy to grind everything down to workable levels, but could human emotions be regulated to such an extent? Paula might not be as amenable as he supposed.

Still, she might be very nice for all that, and it was foolish to be so apprehensive of instincts that warned against meeting her. The truth was, Liza supposed ruefully, that she would much rather have been alone with Grant, the one person she seemed to know at all well, whom she was coming wholly to rely on. But even this whispered unconsciously of danger. Liza gave up.

'I'm sorry,' she murmured, a wave of sheer tiredness enfolding her as his hand came out, touching hers inquiringly.

'And so you should be, my little enigma,' he replied softly, but Liza scarcely heard him. She was asleep.

CHAPTER THREE

THE car's slowing to a halt on reaching Glynsend was so smooth as to be barely perceptible, yet Liza woke up, her nerves still obviously too sensitive.

'Are we here already?' she exclaimed, in some confusion as she struggled upright, half ashamed of her lapse when she had been declaring all along how she couldn't wait to get out of hospital and on to her feet again, in the manner of one positively bursting with a surplus of energy! Why couldn't she have stayed awake? She must have missed a lot of interesting country—something she might have remembered. 'I must have dozed off for a second,' she murmured, naïvely enough to warrant the raising of Grant's dark eyebrows.

'You can say that again,' he teased. 'Just when I was looking forward to a little lively conversation.'

Glancing at him quickly, she was aware he merely joked, an attempt to forestall the apprehension which leapt into her wide green eyes as they swung towards the large, opulent-looking house in front of them. 'Does this belong to you?' she whispered, her tone conveying her utter surprise. She had had in mind a country cottage of very modest proportions—surely he must live most of the time in Town?

'My father left it to me. He bought it before the Second World War when property, by today's standards, was very cheap.'

Which ought to have soothed the little nerves which jerked so sharply in her stomach, but did not. The whole of this seemed to spell more mystery, which she felt she could

41

well do without. It seemed obvious, however, if nothing else
did, that Grant Latham's tolerance only went so far, that he
felt under no compulsion to explain every detail of his
affairs to one of his workers. Judging from the sudden
impatient terseness of his expression he appeared to think
he had already said too much.

He unfastened his seat belt swiftly, then did the same for
hers, placing irritated fingers beneath her chin and turning
her anxious face towards him, not at all tenderly. 'Stop
acting as you imagine a servant should! Such creatures
don't exist today, and in the rare instances where they do,
they have as much self-confidence, if not more, than anyone
else.'

'But I don't know what I was like!' The underlying dryness in his voice disturbed Liza almost as much as his
fingers on her skin. Desperately she wished she could
understand and she glanced downwards rather helplessly,
scared that he might read the apprehension in her eyes instead of the conceit that he sought.

She was unprepared for the impression he did get as her
heavy, silky lashes fluttered and her soft lips parted slightly
on half-formed words. 'I've my suspicions,' he taunted
soberly, 'that when your memory returns you might well
recall you were something of a *femme fatale*!'

His French was impeccable, and she understood. 'No,
never that, I hope!' With a swift, startled jerk, she escaped
his detaining fingers, if not the sharpness of his suddenly
narrowed eyes.

'You could be merely guessing,' was all he said, as he let
her go and got out of the car.

'Come on,' he commanded, opening her door, noting how
she still frowned suspiciously at the house. 'You have so
much the look of a lamb being led to the slaughter that
we'd better get it over and done with. But don't forget,' he
added, his voice hardening, 'that for the length of your stay
you're answerable to no one but me.'

Which could be comforting or otherwise, whichever way
one chose to look at it, Liza decided, nodding numbly as
she walked by his side. His hand, firmly at her elbow, might

have been there for reassurance, but to the people waiting in the wide drawing room it could have been something else, judging from their curious expressions.

Liza saw a woman of about sixty. She could have been more, but the smartness of her dress and make-up might have concealed additional years. On her own she could have been enough, but she was not unexpected. The young man beside her was something quite different. There was nothing remotely elegant about him, unless it was the cut of his well tailored jacket. It was his extreme fairness that caught and held Liza's attention immediately. His hair was fair, almost to the point of whiteness, and his eyes a peculiar light blue which seemed to provide a strange continuity of colour which might either fascinate or repel. Liza only knew a sudden, indescribable urge to touch him, and because such an intensity of feeling startled her she shrank back against Grant, giving every appearance of wishing to cling.

'Come on, Liza,' he urged her firmly forward, yet introducing her slowly, as though to give her time.

Paula Latham's fingers touched Liza's lightly. 'I hope you will enjoy your stay, my dear,' she said, after inquiring casually about Liza's health. 'A little country air can cure almost anything.' She didn't voice any regrets or acknowledge that she might have been any way at fault. Nor did she seem at all sympathetic, and did not even bother to rise from her chair.

But before Liza had time to wonder about this, the young man got up with an alacrity that belied the rather languid expression on his face. Grant introduced him too. 'My stepbrother, Adrian Grey,' he murmured, confounding Liza almost completely, as he had never mentioned him before.

'I'm delighted to meet you.' Adrian's curious blue eyes, so different from Grant's, went over her. 'So you're Grant's latest victim,' he grinned coolly. 'I must say he does pick them!'

'That's enough, Adrian. Even from you!' Grant's eyes glinted, and Adrian appeared to subside, if bitterly.

'Okay, old boy,' he mumbled, 'keep your hair on! I know

better than to quarrel with my bread and butter. Let's just say I was admiring your impeccable taste.'

'I've said, that's enough!' This time Grant's voice came on ice, leaving Liza with the distinct impression of enmity between the two brothers. Yet they were not brothers at all, surely? Not even related except for the ties of Paula's marriage. Adrian must have been the son of her first husband, before she had met Grant's father. He was so clearly impertinent, quite different from Grant, yet he drew her in spite of herself. There was something about his colouring which affected her strangely, and she didn't care for this new confusion of feelings. Surely she couldn't be a bit of a siren, as Grant had suggested in the car—because Grant attracted her too, if in an entirely different way. A way which her mind rejected, refused to consider seriously for even a moment.

Grant was continuing levelly, as though while he did not approve of Adrian's vagueness he was used to it, 'I thought you were staying on in Rome. What brought you back home so suddenly?'

'Paula.' Adrian's narrow shoulders shrugged as he glanced briefly towards his mother. 'She doesn't like my being away, and it doesn't actually make much difference to me where I am. I'm afraid your brainwave didn't produce anything very rewarding, my dear Grant. My mind remained as unco-operative in that fair city as it does here.'

Liza glanced quickly from one to the other. Grant's quick frown added to the mystery. Why did he want Adrian away from home?

Grant was saying, 'You could have been better advised to have waited. Nothing is ever achieved without patience.' His sardonic glance swung to Paula who, as if anticipating his imminent attack, spoke quickly.

'I really do need Adrian here, Grant, or rather I do feel he needs me. When he's out of my sight I worry . . .'

'Good God!' The exclamation broke from Grant tersely. 'He's all of twenty-nine!'

'And you've never lost the superiority of your extra seven

years, have you, Grant?' Paula's voice rose plaintively. 'I know what Adrian's needs are.'

'But you don't know what's good for him.'

'No? I'm simply his mother . . . !'

'And we simply don't exist!' Adrian murmured in a low aside to Liza as she stood, apparently forgotten, as Grant exchanged impatient words with Paula.

'You, I could have done without!' Overhearing, Grant swung on Adrian curtly, speaking with such absolute assurance that Adrian flinched, flushing a dull red. But before Liza could feebly intervene, Grant's eyes fixed on her sharply, noting the air of fine exhaustion on her face. 'I'll take you up to your room, Liza. You look about all in. No, Paula,' he said decisively, as Paula started to her feet, 'I want to see for myself that she's in the room I ordered. It wouldn't be the first time my instructions have been misconstrued. We can continue our discussion when I come down.'

Because she didn't know what else to do, Liza allowed herself to be led from the room. She couldn't say she wasn't glad to escape such tangible undercurrents as she could clearly feel here, but a thread of curiosity ran through her regarding the whole situation. She was forced to confess, although she didn't yet understand it, that Adrian Grey, with his morose, seemingly embittered personality, aroused her interest.

Grant took her up the beautiful old staircase, along a wide corridor into a large bedroom on the first floor. Liza, still confused by the huge scale of everything, wondered uneasily if she would ever get used to it. The bedroom was beautiful but, even on a warm September evening, felt chill with disuse. Grant must have felt it too, as with an impatient gesture his fingers went out to press the bell. 'Fools!' Liza heard him mutter coldly beneath his breath.

Within a few moments a servant came running. 'I wasn't told anything about this room, sir!' Her sharp brown eyes immediately took in the situation. 'I've prepared the blue room at the end of the east corridor.'

'On whose orders?' Grant asked grimly.

'Well, Mrs Latham's, sir. She thought it would be cosier. Perhaps the young lady herself would like it better there?'

He ignored this and merely gave the woman a withering glance, and used a tone which was so unfamiliar as to make Liza quake. 'Make up this bed immediately, Mrs Brown. Miss Dean has been ill and is tired. She must rest.'

As the woman ran to do his bidding he bent down to turn up the heating. 'It will soon warm up,' he smiled at Liza, the coolness leaving his voice. 'I don't think you'll take any harm.'

'No, I'm sure I shan't,' she smiled back, relieved to see the last of his barely suppressed aggression, and disregarding the sudden notion that she should be familiar with it. She was beginning to grow weary of these elusive notions which were springing to her mind more frequently, presumably trying to speak of some past experience but with nothing more than a transient background flicker to back them up.

Glancing swiftly at Grant, she could see he was still faintly annoyed. As he prowled restlessly to the window she stared, frowning, at his dark head, etched against the late summer twilight. It must be because this room wasn't ready, but such mistakes were easily made, and she had little doubt that the blue room would have done very well.

'I don't want to cause any bother,' she said nervously, saying the very thing apparently guaranteed to stimulate his dying wrath.

'Liza!' But his angrily impatient exclamation was cut short as Mrs Brown panted back to them, carrying a pile of crisp linen. Following her came a man with Liza's suitcases. Liza watched wonderingly as the man deposited several pieces of expensive pigskin luggage, lightly saluting Grant as he dropped them down. 'Is there anything more you require, sir?'

'Nothing for the moment, Carter,' Grant replied calmly. 'I'll see you when I finish here.'

Liza stared at him, but the dark eyes gazing back were unreadable, and he turned away. Who were all these people? she wondered dismally. Surely this was not the

normal household of a small shopkeeper, successful though
he might be? What an idiot she must have been when, for a
few moments in his car before she fell asleep, she had seen
herself helping Paula prepare Grant's evening meal! How
he must be laughing at her, because of course, with his
lightning astuteness, he must have read her foolish mind.

Unhappily convinced of her own stupidity, Liza collapsed into a nearby chair, her legs refusing to support her
any longer. To be an object of his ridicule seemed almost
the last straw, and fervently she began to wish she had
never let herself be persuaded to come here. He must only
think her a nuisance! But surprisingly his voice was devoid
of any mockery when, after watching Mrs Brown moodily
for a short while, he glanced at Liza again almost tenderly.

'I'll look in later,' he said, 'after dinner. You'll have
something light up here. Our local GP is to see you tomorrow, so he mustn't find you any the worse. Mrs Brown will
help you into bed.'

Silently Liza watched him go without the energy to protest, even if he had been inclined to listen, which she very
much doubted! Besides, he seemed to know her almost
better than she knew herself. She felt so tired that she was
entirely glad to submit gratefully to Mrs Brown's gently
efficient hands, to forget the way her heart was beginning to
beat so much swifter every time she came under the surveillance of Grant Latham's dark eyes.

She must have dozed, wakening only to hear Mrs Brown
returning with her dinner. It was delicious, but she found
herself able to take just a little of the thin soup before
pushing it away. She still felt tired and weak, almost tearful
again, the sense of isolation caused by the loss of her
memory pressing down on her in a new, frightening fashion.
It had been something hard to bear in hospital where there
had always been someone, nurses and doctors, coming and
going, but here there was no sound, nothing to distract her.
Darkness outside, and a rather terrifying quietness within.
Suddenly she longed for Grant.

And as if by magic he appeared, instantly taking the
weight of her despair. 'I have your tablets,' he said as he

opened the door and strode towards her.

'You could have left them before.' Whatever happened he mustn't be allowed to guess how much she was coming to depend on him.

He stood staring down at her as she lay, pale and lovely, her hair tumbled like a living flame across the pillows, the thin sheet pulled up over her slender body. Aware instantly of her returning apprehension, his eyes narrowed, and he didn't point out, as she had gloomily expected him to, that she might not have remembered how many to take. Instead he smiled mildly, reducing the sudden tension between them to more manageable levels.

'Perhaps you haven't guessed how I enjoy a sense of responsibility,' he teased. 'Anyway, I don't suppose you're going to need them much longer.'

'Nor you,' she gasped painfully, rejecting him deliberately out of hand, her taut young face, for one unguarded moment, vividly portraying her inner agitation, an abject denial of what she had said.

Grant sat down on the edge of the bed like a man with a firm grip on himself, while the swiftly-dowsed smoulder at the back of his midnight blue eyes might have concealed a flicker of studied satisfaction at the too-obvious state of her emotions. 'We are all of us necessary at some time or another,' he agreed lightly, reaching calmly for her glass of water, 'but it's also just as true that none of us are indispensable either.'

For a moment Liza felt overcome with gratitude without knowing why. Compared to the fever raging within her, his words, his whole manner, were notably cool, but steadying, she had to admit. He was offering her back her pride and she grasped it, searching rapidly for a safer subject—anything!

'Grant,' she struggled upright, taking the tablets he counted out without further argument, along with a quick gulp of water, 'you didn't tell me you had a brother.'

'You didn't ask about my family, not that I can recall,' he countered dryly, taking the glass from her clenched fingers and setting it down on the small table by the bed.

'And he's not my brother, as you must have guessed. He is in fact Paula's son. He came to live here when she married my father. Later Adrian married my cousin.'

'He's married?' Where, Liza wondered, was this cousin, his wife?

'Phoebe died two years ago,' Grant's mouth twisted wryly. 'Adrian's been no good ever since.'

Liza frowned sympathetically, not caring for the hardness of Gran't expression. 'Two years isn't so very long.'

His eyes creased ironically. 'A lifetime wouldn't be long enough in some cases. We surely owe something to the living as well as the dead—we can't always entirely please ourselves. He keeps Paula in a constant state of anxiety. He had a successful career, which he ought to be thinking of seriously again.'

'What does he do?' It was slightly comforting to know that there were other lost people in the world besides herself.

'He writes.'

Grant's brief replies might indicate a reluctance to discuss Adrian, but there was no reason why Liza should feel herself suddenly flinch. Instantly alert to her changing moods, Grant watched her face closely. 'Maybe you've read some of his books?'

'Possibly,' she nodded, gratefully grasping the explanation. 'If I saw one tomorrow, perhaps I could tell.'

'A small, harmless exercise for that regrettable memory,' he agreed lightly. 'Anyway, it's a thought and shows a healthy desire to recover,' he teased. He hesitated, his voice degrees cooler. 'But don't overdo the sympathy, my dear. Adrian gets too much of that from Paula as it is.'

'And you don't think it's a good antidote?' she commented, too wryly.

His blue eyes studied her. There was a resigned curve to the corners of her beautifully shaped mouth which made him aware that unconsciously perhaps she applied the question also to herself. He said, his voice tinged with a faint amusement, 'Not when illness reaches a certain stage. I'm no doctor, but I should have thought something more bracing might achieve better results.'

'Such as?' Her anxious gaze stayed on his dark face, shadowed with uncertainty.

His eyes, dark pools of mockery, glinted as he suddenly reached over and kissed her tremulous lips. 'You did ask,' he said softly, 'and a demonstration often proves better than words. Only I'm not advising you to try it with Adrian. That young man must work out his own destiny. God knows he's had enough help!'

Liza had, not surprisingly, forgotten all about Adrian. There was no thought of him on her tautly indrawn breath. Grant's mouth had been gentle, but so clearly not enough. She had an overwhelming desire to be kissed properly—by him. Her senses clamoured, aroused to distraction by even so light a touch, and a pulse beat swiftly, betrayingly visible at the base of her smooth, white throat. Involuntarily her hands lifted, to grasp his arms as he bent across her as if obeying the blind dictates of her body. 'Grant,' she whispered, her mouth shaking, her voice a soft invitation.

For a long moment he stared at her, his glance narrowed, obviously holding himself with no small amount of restraint as he gently released her clinging hands. 'Goodnight, infant,' was all he said.

'Infant!' she repeated, her voice weak, noticeably under the weight of his apparent indifference. She didn't like the sound of it one bit. If she had been an infant she certainly didn't feel like one now! Not since he had kissed her! Her green eyes widening, she gazed up at him reproachfully. He was too attractive, but didn't he realise she had no real wish to resist him?

But it seemed that as usual he could read the thoughts moving so painfully through her uncertain eyes, and would use his own methods of dealing with them. 'Yes, infant,' he emphasised, softly adamant. 'That's the way it's going to be for a while yet. But don't let it upset you, there's a time coming...'

Which could be interpreted in many different ways, all of which Liza felt suddenly too tired to consider. Grant talked of time enigmatically, as though he had her entire future mapped out. All she had to do was simply follow the prescribed routes, which naturally would be of his choosing. Wholly acquiescent in that moment, Liza let her heavy lashes droop on her damp cheeks.

'You think about it,' she heard him advising gently, his hand smoothing back her tumbled hair from her flushed face.

Sleepily reassured, she half smiled at him, her parted lips unconsciously seductive, but completely trusting.

'I'll see you in the morning,' he said, and rose abruptly from the bed, deliberately switching off the main light, his actions those of a man whose mind is on other things.

During the weekend Grant was with her frequently, but Liza saw little of either Paula or Adrian. Paula slept late, she was told, not usually appearing until it was time for lunch.

Which seemed such an absolute waste of such wonderful weather, Liza decided as she sat in the garden. She had spent the greater part of the morning in the garden. The doctor had been and gone, after pronouncing himself satisfied. Liza, eager to have a look outside, had tiptoed to the window after he had gone and seen him having a long conversation with Grant on the drive below, but as they were obviously on very friendly terms this did not seem surprising. They were probably discussing the weather or fishing, not her.

Lying beneath a huge willow tree on a very comfortable recliner, Liza had to admit that Grant was being extremely kind. The doctor had said that fresh air would do her nothing but good when she had pleaded to be allowed to go out, and after she had finished dressing, Grant had brought her here, on to the lawn, sharing with her the coffee Mrs Brown had carried to them and placed on a low cane table at their side. Later, although it was Saturday, he had gone to his study to work, and she had lain and watched the river flowing by.

It was so peaceful that she felt she could have stayed for

ever gazing on the idly running water, listening to the soft rustle of leaves above her head. A conscious gratitude towards Grant stirred continually, a total confidence in his ability to make everything right for her, so that she found herself relaxing, for the moment not resenting the frightening blank spaces of her mind.

The sensation was oddly metamorphic, the tension that had held her over the past weeks seeming to leave her to such an extent that she felt quite resentful when Adrian Grey appeared.

It grew even more pronounced when, without so much as a by-your-leave, he sat down beside her in the chair only recently vacated by Grant. 'So you're the young heroine of the fire?' he said sarcastically, as though they had never met. His eyes travelled lightly over her slender face and body, as any man's might have done, but the usual appreciation was missing. No real interest lay in his blankly assessing glance; his face was dull, devoid of any real expression. Liza realised, with almost a start, he had no curiosity left, that he was plainly bored with everything, even living.

'Oh, no!' she cried, wholly shocked to find such an uncaring rejection of life in one who could only be a few years older than herself. Well, nine or ten, she thought.

'And what was that all about?' Adrian opened his eyes which he had idly been about to close, such an emphatic exclamation taking his attention in spite of himself. It could have nothing to do with his own opening gambit, which never warranted such a startled reply.

'Why, nothing.' Liza coloured while she searched wildly for a suitable explanation. How could one possibly express such an intimate impression in words? One couldn't say You looked like a man who has lost his soul to a more or less complete stranger!

'You were just thinking aloud then,' he grinned, and suddenly even appeared to surprise himself by sitting up and taking notice. 'Perhaps you felt happier on your own, you didn't want my company?'

'No,' she said hastily, 'it wasn't that.'

'You don't seem to object to Grant's,' he interrupted morosely. 'But then women never do! Of course if I had everything he's got ...'

Coolly Liza glanced at him, observing the note of self-pity Grant had warned her about, even while she tried to ignore Adrian's exact words. 'From what I hear,' she said quickly, 'you have plenty going for you.'

'Hearsay,' he muttered scornfully, 'always hearsay!' He slumped again in his chair, no longer diverted. 'I suppose you've already heard about how I am? How I'm wasting my not inconsiderable talents, how I ought to snap out of it. The list could be never-ending!'

'Grant told me you used to write,' she replied cautiously, but more eagerly than she knew. Illogically something inside her toyed and clung, developed a little preoccupation with an art that seemed to tantalise her memory in some very definite way.

'I did write, Liza,' suddenly Adrian was speaking savagely. 'Books people enjoyed. Clever scientific mysteries, mostly set abroad, which took months to set up, from all sorts of angles, but guaranteed to keep my readers enthralled! Is it my fault I can't do it any more? That my brain refuses to function in certain directions at all? I'm not even capable of stringing two sentences together, let alone a book. Have you ever loved and lost, Liza Dean, or know of people who have? Because if you haven't, you can't possibly know what I'm talking about!'

His words hit her, hurting like sharp pieces of granite, and she stared at him aghast. 'Oh, but I do—at least——' Numbly she hesitated, coming up against the now familiar blank. What had she known? Those few illuminating seconds had shown her a door opening, only to have it slammed abruptly in her face again.

Helplessly she shuddered, her distress so patently obvious as to jerk Adrian momentarily from his own slough of despond. 'I'm sorry, Liza. I was forgetting that you have been ill.' His awkwardly expressed sympathy pointed to his usual self-centred inability to see any other problems but his own, but his brief apology sounded sincere enough as his eyes rested curiously on Liza's whitening face. 'I suppose,' he shrugged wryly, 'you must have enough troubles of your own.'

'Well,' she copied his shrug, 'at least I don't remember mine.'

'Which could be a mixed blessing,' Adrian pondered. 'If I could forget some of the things that plague me I might feel better. But not being able to recall anything must make life deuced awkward at times.'

'You can say that again!'

'So emphatic,' he grinned, as if genuinely amused by the way her soft voice rose indignantly. 'There can't be a lot in your young life that might be better forgotten, but there could be exciting possibilities. People and events, just crying out for total recall!'

'Such as . . .?' Liza had lost much of her faith in any such possibilities, but glancing quickly towards him she saw with some surprise that he looked almost animated, as if something in her story had stirred a dormant imagination. It would be nice to think that, even inadvertently, she could help someone.

Adrian's eyebrows were rising consideringly over her query. 'A boy-friend, perhaps?'

'I don't think so.' She felt vaguely disappointed. 'If there had been he would surely have been making some inquiries before now? Besides, they would have known at the shop.'

'Of course.' He lay back, apparently losing interest. 'I was forgetting you worked at the—er—shop!'

The silence was, on Liza's side, suddenly breathless, 'Adrian,' she asked, 'have you ever been to the shop?'

'What a foolish question!'

'Yes, I realise, but . . .'

'But what?'

She had an idea that for reasons of his own he was hedging, and she knew a surge of impatience. He surely didn't imagine she was going to ask embarrassing questions merely to satisfy an idle curiosity! 'I simply wondered what it was like. He hasn't—I mean, I haven't liked to ask Grant outright.'

'And you haven't been back since your accident?'

'No.'

'Well, what is it you want to know exactly? Surely, with such an air of beautiful innocence, you aren't indirectly wondering how much Grant is worth?'

'Of course not!' His sheer brutality hit her so that she wanted to get up and run away, but miserably she subsided. Her being here at all could seem very suspicious to any casual observer. Uncertainty flickered through her wide green eyes. 'You'll just have to believe I haven't wondered about any such thing, not in the horrible way you suggest, although I have to admit this house has shaken me.'

'Liza!' Those who knew Adrian Grey these days might have been surprised at the feeling in his loud exclamation. 'I'm sorry again if I've hurt you! If you could stop speaking in riddles and explain clearly, I might begin to understand.'

Liza flushed. A veritable mountain seemed to be growing out of a molehill, and she wished fervently she had never said anything to start with. 'It's really nothing,' she mumbled, 'it's only that Grant's been so good to me and I'm not sure that he can afford it. He can't make all that much out of one shop, especially if he has a house like this to keep up.'

'Ha!' Adrian's shout of laughter shook her. 'Was that what he told you? So much on your poor conscience! Now, I suppose, you're ready to launch into me about being a lazy hanger-on. Poor Grant!'

Infuriated, Liza stared at him, her pleasure in the morning rapidly evaporating. 'I can't think why you should find that so funny!'

'Can't you, Liza?' Adrian wiped his eyes. 'Do you know, I do believe I'm going to enjoy your visit. I've never felt so amused since—well, it doesn't matter . . .'

'Since your wife died, perhaps?' Adrian didn't seem to believe in sparing other people's feelings so why should she consider his? 'Before she died, I mean.'

'Probably.'

His reply came lightly, but instantly Liza felt a twinge of

remorse. She shouldn't have said that, yet no one enjoyed feeling like a positive source of amusement. 'Grant is working in his study right now,' she exclaimed indignantly. 'I shouldn't like to think he was having to put in extra hours just to keep me, even though your own conscience appears relatively untroubled!'

At this sharply thrown remark, Adrian simply roared. Like water off a duck's back, Liza decided acidly, without knowing where such an expression came from.

'I can see,' he quipped, rubbing his eyes, 'we're going to get on, you and I! But first you must allow me to straighten you out a bit about Grant. In London he owns one or two—I suppose you could call them shops, and he has others in almost every town in the land.' Adrian hesitated, as if uncertain whether to divulge all, but at the dawning apprehension on Liza's face, was unable to resist adding, 'He could nicely afford to keep half a dozen poor little shopgirls without so much as blinking an eyelid, and an equal number of pathetic stepbrothers like myself. Why do you suppose, my dear, that I'm not greatly perturbed about my missing urge to work? Grant would never see me starve, for Phoebe's sake, if nothing else. Maybe it might be better for me if he did.'

Afterwards Liza felt anger, but at the time, listening to Adrian's startling disclosures, she felt nothing but shock. Why had Grant not told her? It could have been easy for him to have done this lightly, instead of allowing her to go on believing he was almost as poor as a church mouse. That he had left it to someone like Adrian to mention seemed the end! Even now, as her jarred nerves jerked her to her feet, she prayed there might be some mistake, and without stopping to do more than throw a fraught glance at Adrian's surprised face she turned from him and rushed towards the house.

After more than three weeks of inactivity, her legs felt curiously weak, and her reserve of breath almost non-existent. She was exhausted before she reached the hall and found a servant to direct her to Grant's study.

Without knocking she thrust open the door, but it was only as she stood facing him that she realised she didn't have a thing to say. Hadn't she been utterly foolhardy? Rushing like a mad thing into a man's house to accuse him of being secretive about his own business. Something which could have nothing to do with her!

As swiftly as she had flown in, she twisted to fly out, but she hadn't reckoned on how quickly Grant would move to forestall her. Dropping the telephone he was holding, he was beside her in a flash, his hands pouncing on her shaking shoulders.

'What the devil!' His voice was curt, loaded with an admirable restraint not reflected in his glinting eyes. 'What in heaven's name got into you, Liza?'

She liked him, in that instant, no better than she had liked Adrian when he had made his soul-shattering disclosures. 'Just let me go,' she gasped. 'I made a mistake in ever coming here!'

'A remark which is not, I think, confined to my study?' His eyes fixed on her hotly flushed cheeks, the flaming mane of tumbled hair that fanned out wildly, and for a moment as they stared furiously into each other's eyes, it seemed they were transferred to another place and time, enacting a scene that had in some way been familiar.

'Oh, no ...!' Liza's voice rose almost to a scream as something hurt her. 'Take your hands off me!' she sobbed, thinking she had found the source of her pain.

'It's not my hands,' he said, obviously remembering something Liza did not, and, instinctively aware of this, she cried, hysterically thwarted.

'Another secret? Something else you'd rather not tell me?'

'Liza!' Now he was shaking her, and this time his fingers really hurt as they found the soft skin beneath the fine cotton of her dress. Then he was lifting her slumped body, placing her firmly in a deep chair by the side of the slow burning fire. 'Come on,' he coaxed, brushing the heavy hair back from her forehead, a gesture which he accomplished with his usual deftness as he flicked it behind her small ears before dropping a lightly reassuring kiss on her trembling mouth. 'Won't you tell me all about it?'

'You don't have to treat me like a child!'

'So you said last night, but don't tempt me,' he retorted grimly, but naturally she mistook his meaning and flushed.

'You've been talking to Adrian,' he went on, 'I noticed when I looked out before to see if you were all right.'

'Yes,' she glanced at Grant swiftly. So he hadn't deserted her as she had thought, but how could one accuse a man of being well off, as though it was a crime? It could seem indescribably impertinent.

'You'd better begin,' he suggested sardonically, not, it seemed, prepared to spare her, 'and don't waste any more time considering how you're going to. Out with it!'

CHAPTER FOUR

UNEASILY Liza stirred, without one really clear idea in her head as to where she could begin. If she had allowed a reckless impulsiveness to drive her here, she was now paying for it; she couldn't think of one thing to say!

Had she always been like this, she wondered, too impetuous for her own good? She had only just met Adrian and had nothing more than his slender evidence to go on. He could have been deliberately provoking her, men in his condition often indulged in a little mischief, if merely to inflict on others something of their own uncertainty. Or did they? Where had such a notion come from? No, she suspected that Adrian had been nearer the mark than she was willing to allow. It was Grant who had deliberately misled her!

'You ought to have told me!' she exclaimed at last, lifting her eyes to stare up at him as he sat carelessly on the broad arm of her chair, facing her, his dark face impassive with mock patience as he waited for her to make up her mind.

'Told you what?' he sighed coolly, as if the continuous repetition of her opening sentence was beginning to bore him.

The room swayed a little around her and she drew a quick gasping breath. 'That you own so much! That you aren't poor.' Now it was out Liza was convinced she sounded dreadful. She added quickly, as if to allay such an impression, 'How you must have enjoyed seeing me make such a fool of myself!'

Grant's blue eyes narrowed into silver slits, and for a moment he looked quite frightening, but otherwise, apart

59

from the tensing of the powerful muscles in his bare fore-
arms as he leant over her, there was no indication of his
anger. 'Adrian has been telling you this?'

'Not deliberately.' Grant's annoyance came through with
his taut breath on her face, and instinctively she sought to
protect Adrian from it. 'I think he sensed I was worried
about being an expense you couldn't afford when I asked
about your shop.'

'And that's been bothering you, hasn't it, Liza?' Grant's
expression was quickly cruel. 'You couldn't leave it alone.
Instead of concentrating on getting better you've been
applying all your energy to getting to the bottom of something which has never been your business!'

'I'm sorry, Mr Latham.' Aghast, her eyes flickered away
from him. She hadn't seen him like this before, though
she had guessed there would be a harder side to him than
any he had so far shown her. Could she dispute the truth of
what he said? Daily she seemed to think of little but Grant
and his shop; the idea of him struggling with a small,
inflation-hit business had worried her out of her head. But
somehow, to know that he too must have problems, if rather
dissimilar ones to her own, had seemed, maybe crazily, to
suggest that they had something in common. Now, when
she realised how far removed he must be from her own
position as a comparatively humble assistant, she could only
squirm with a growing humiliation! 'I'm extremely sorry,
Mr Latham,' this time she repeated his name with emphasis, intending it as an apology for her unwonted temerity,
an oblique reassurance that she wouldn't trespass again.

'Mr Latham!' Grant sounded depressingly harsh when
his white teeth clamped and he spoke between them. Liza
shivered, but he went on, regardless of her widening green
eyes, her nervousness merely serving to arouse his funda-
mental impatience, 'So much for the confidence I've tried
to build up! Of course I could have told you about my
affairs, explained them in detail, but what good do you
imagine it would have done? You needed someone, you
were like a soul wrecked on a desert island—still are, if it
comes to that! If you'd been left entirely alone or, on the

other hand, filled up with a lot of facts which might have distressed you, would you ever have survived?'

'I'd have had to,' she cried restively. 'It couldn't have been impossible.'

'Well, you didn't have to, did you?' He was suddenly more formidable than she would have thought possible as he came closer, so close that she could almost feel the warmth of his body and she was aware of the clean, male scent of him. 'But now you know—so we don't have any more secrets. If I have transgressed you can put it down to an outsize attack of conscience.'

'Conscience?' The sarcasm in his voice was hard to bear.

'About the fire, my dear. Don't pretend you'd forgotten the relevant facts.'

'Only that?' The query was out, along with an almost tearful despondency, before she could stop it.

'For the moment.' He ignored her shimmering eyes. 'But in discovering my duplicity, don't feel too superior, Miss Dean. Remember, you might have worse skeletons in your own cupboard when your memory returns.'

Her head drooped as it so often did when she was anxious, and her hot brow seemed naturally to come to rest against his arm. 'I'm sorry, Grant,' she whispered weakly, deserting *Mr Latham* once and for all, her remorse too apparent as she momentarily closed her heavy eyes. 'I owe you so much. I shouldn't have talked about you to anyone!'

'Never mind,' his voice was suddenly softer, his hand curving her nape, his thumb soothing the satiny skin of her ear and cheek, the pressure just enough to make her aware of it, to remind her gently that one day he might seek a certain kind of repayment. 'I'm not going to pretend,' he continued, tracing the line of colour that flared enchantingly under his probing fingers, 'that I approve of your confiding in Adrian, but I have no doubt Paula would have enlightened you. She excels at such things, and women tend to exaggerate more than men. The actual size of my business is something I often overlook, but I promise to try and explain it to you one day soon.'

Liza was suddenly beset by a reluctance to reply, to

speak at all, or even move, never to open her eyes and find him staring down at her, perhaps impatiently. This way, with her eyes closed as she leaned against him, she could feel the insidious sensation from his hands moving irresistibly through her with an intensity she found hard to withstand. He might not realise how he was beginning to affect her, but the thought came to her spinning head that he did know, and acted deliberately. But it was still hard to take a deeply denying breath, to force herself upright, away from him.

'I don't think I need know any more, Grant,' she replied. 'I certainly don't have any right to the finer details. It would be quite ridiculous to think I had.'

'Would it?' His slight smile was suddenly enigmatical, but he made no further attempt to restrain her. Instead he rose to his feet with an audible sigh, a glance down his straight nose at her. 'I've work to do,' he shrugged dryly, 'and you're proving too much of a distraction. You'd better sit there quietly until I've at least finished off what I was busy with when you so inconveniently interrupted. Then we'll have a drink before lunch and I'd better keep an eye on you for the rest of the weekend.'

He did, and the weekend passed quietly, and on Sunday, after dinner, Paula said, 'I don't suppose we will be seeing you next weekend, Grant.'

He glanced at her levelly over the gilded rim of his coffee cup. 'I'll be down tomorrow evening, Paula, no later than six-thirty, so you won't have to wait dinner.'

Liza, who happened to be looking at Paula, saw her start. 'Good gracious, Grant,' she laughed, although she didn't sound terribly amused, 'whatever for? Has Adrian's return from Rome...'

'It has nothing to do with Adrian's return from Rome or anywhere else,' he cut in firmly, eyeing Adrian grimly. 'You appear to forget, Paula, he's a big boy now. No, among other things, I am in the throes of enlarging a branch on the south coast, and can in fact manage that from here more easily than from London.'

Paula seemed unconvinced. 'But you do everything from

London,' she protested, staring at him, clearly puzzled, her frowning gaze fixed on his handsome features.

'Since when did I have to explain my every movement?' he drawled, with what Liza privately considered was undue sarcasm, the smoothness of his words belying any real politeness.

'Oh, really, Grant!' Quite clearly Paula recognised the limits he set, but a slight flush mounted her over-powdered cheeks. 'I wasn't prying. I simply got it into my head you might be worrying over much about Adrian—or Liza.' For almost the first time that evening she looked at Liza directly. 'But you know we'll take good care of her, won't we, Adrian?' Effusively she smiled at her son's indifferent face as he stood idly beside the window.

Paula's eagerness was too artificial. Liza glanced at her before her gaze swung to Adrian, who shrugged, obviously not prepared to enter into the argument one way or another, as he turned to gaze again out over the gardens.

Liza sighed. She had a profound suspicion Paula didn't like her, and wished rather fervently that she had stayed upstairs. It was Grant who had insisted she came down for dinner that evening, for the first time, and, although on Friday and Saturday she had been faintly resentful when he had sent her back to bed after tea like some small child, she had been full of strange misgivings when Grant had said that afternoon, 'If you promise to retire early, without any argument, you can put on something pretty and come down again later. It will be a change for you to dine with us, and I don't think, now you're a little stronger, that you will come to any harm.'

It had taken Liza a long time to choose something suitable from the array of gowns she now possessed in her wardrobe. She had searched for something demure, feeling nervously that the soft, more sophisticated dresses were not her style. Eventually she had found one, simply cut with a gently bouffant skirt and softly belted waist, in the palest of summer greens, which wasn't really a colour at all until she had put it on.

She had taken so long that she might have been late if

Grant hadn't walked in as she was rather desperately trying to do up the zip.

'I'll help you with that,' he had said, both the way he entered her room and his tone of voice proprietorial, but she had been in too much of a dither, too pleased to have his assistance, to notice.

She had turned to him her slender, pale back automatically, as if it was the most usual thing in the world to have a man walk into her room when she was no more than half dressed. It was only as she felt his knuckles hard against her bare skin as he manipulated the stiff fastening that she had flinched with startled awareness, a tremor running madly right through her.

If Grant had felt her almost visible quiver, he had given no indication. 'No make-up?' he had queried lightly, his hands, completing their task, sliding to her shoulders, his eyes scrutinising her flushed face as they were both reflected in the wide mirror.

Liza's hair had already been brushed and tumbled heavy and shining, a most wonderful shade of red, about her slim neck, but she hadn't got round yet to any further embellishment. She wasn't exactly sure what she had needed.

'Try a little something on your eyes,' he had suggested, as if reading her uncertain thoughts while he studied the clear-cut line of her facial structure expertly. Objectively was the word, Liza supposed as obediently, without apparently a will of her own, she had smoothed on a minute dot of soft shadow and picked up a wand of dark mascara. The effect had been rather startling, making her eyes seem instantly huge, with the mysterious green of shadowed water, and she had noticed Grant nod approvingly.

'Now a little lipstick,' he had smiled, but with determination in his glance as he waited, watching as she had searched with some confusion through the positive array of unused make-up in front of her. She could only guess where it had all come from; certainly she had no recollection of buying any of it herself. It must be just one more thing she had to thank Grant for. This and her new wardrobe of clothes, all of which looked expensive. Still, most of them she hoped she wouldn't need to wear, and they could always go back to the shop.

Eventually she found a shade of lipstick that she had thought would do, and again he had watched as she tried to apply it. But her hand had suddenly been shaking so much that she couldn't manage, and with an impatient gesture Grant had taken it from her and, turning her face round, had applied it to her lips himself.

'Keep still!' Her quickly indrawn breath had parted her soft lips, and his dark brows drew together warningly, instantly controlling her desire to get up and flee. The hand that held her head firmly had tightened, as if he had been fully aware of her urge to escape. 'This won't take long,' he had said, 'but if I leave you to do it yourself you might never get downstairs this evening.'

There was no doubt he was something of an expert, in spite of his flippant words. His movements had been swift and deft, masterly, with a decision she could never hope to fight and a dangerous ability to awaken all kinds of emotions, to set her nerves clamouring. The breath Liza had drawn in so swiftly still hadn't been let out!

'You have a beautiful mouth,' he had commented, studying his finished work with no little satisfaction before bending his head, as if seeking to convince her by softly kissing her lips.

Unable to stop herself, Liza had felt her body sway towards him, her hands sliding up to his neck in a wholly undeniable attempt to hold him closer, but with the same restraint he had exercised the previous day in his study, Grant had grasped her fragile wrists, and pushed her gently away. 'You wouldn't want to undo all my good work, would you?' he had mocked, smiling at her too urgent response to what on his part had merely been intended as a lightly reassuring caress.

'I don't know how you do it,' Liza had gasped, managing somehow to borrow some of his own carelessness, even though her heart was pounding.

'You mean my expertise with a lipstick?' he had asked, suddenly so cynical that she'd shivered. 'In my trade, Liza,' he had shrugged, 'you have to know about such things, but this is actually the first time I've tried my hand at it personally. I had a secretary once who, whenever I stopped dictating, reached automatically for her make-up. I got to thinking she was better at that than anything else.'

'She isn't with you now?'

'No, it was a long time ago.'

In the seconds it had taken for Liza's pulse to settle again Grant had looked her slowly up and down, and she had known with a peculiar certainty that, while he might consider women desirable, he also considered they were there to be used, and cast off when a man tired of them! Women had undoubtedly spoiled him by letting him see all too clearly the effect he had on them, yet he was essentially a man with a compelling force within him that was hard to resist. A force which would always insist a woman must obey, without any visible sign that she possessed any will of her own.

Recalling how he had removed her too clinging arms, Liza felt hot with a shameful embarrassment. However—she tried to take a long, cool look at the matter—with a man like Grant she could be totally out of her depth, so it was perhaps just as well he was inclined to repel her rather juvenile enthusiasm.

But the crisply approving nod with which he had surveyed her completed elegance had proved little consolation to a heart that had remained curiously unsatisfied.

Paula Latham, at dinner, had taken little real notice of Liza, but at the same time Liza noticed she missed very little, her eyes darting restlessly everywhere. Her son was her obsessive interest, it wasn't difficult to see, but Adrian appeared to regard his mother with a tolerant indifference which she was unaware of, or was determined to ignore. It had appeared to surprise her that he often stared at Liza moodily, but then, as Adrian's attention puzzled Liza just as much, she couldn't have accounted for it, even should Paula have asked her.

Liza, in turn, found something about Adrian Grey oddly intriguing. It wasn't, she felt, a personal attraction, such as she knew when she looked at Grant. It was more an indefinable feeling that she could in no way understand, no matter how hard she concentrated.

Grant had sat at the head of the table, tall and sophisticated, curiously unapproachable, matching the dark elegance of the dining room, and Liza had found it easier to talk to Adrian, whose homely features seemed so much less frightening.

Greatly daring, she had asked several pertinent questions about his books, and was greatly delighted when he very civilly answered every one of them. He had even, when she could think of nothing more to ask, gone on to explain expansively about the very first one he had written, amusing her so much that she had seemed to dissolve into a series of giggles, and even Paula's perpetually frowning face had broken into a faintly indulgent smile.

Grant had been no more than ordinarily polite, and if he had listened to Adrian, had refrained from comment, addressing most of his conversation to Paula as if seeking to divert a little of her preoccupation with her son. But Liza had felt his dark gaze often on her averted profile, and if her light laughter was sometimes a little forced, she only hoped he didn't guess. Where Grant was concerned a barrier of some sort had to be erected, yet now that the weekend was almost over, the thought of his departure for London, of not perhaps seeing him for several days, seemed too much to be borne.

So it was his emphatic announcement over coffee that he intended to return the next evening that jerked Liza's wide-eyed gaze back to him with a warmer glow in her heart than she had known over the past hour, despite Adrian's entertaining conversation. The positive paean of relief in her eyes as she had stared at Grant might have told an observant onlooker that while Adrian might arouse her curiosity, emotionally she felt nothing for him at all!

If Liza was startled by the depth of her own feelings, she simply put it down to the fact that she had come to depend on Grant almost completely. Anyone else she could perhaps do without, but not him. Such a revelation could be nothing

less than startling, and for a moment Liza's gaze dropped
to the table, her bewildered eyes on the delicate lace mats,
the gleaming silver and glass, without really seeing them. It
might be better if Grant did stay away all week—it could
have given her a chance to discover herself. Exactly what
she meant by this Liza would have been hard put to explain. It could be that by relying so much on Grant's
authority she didn't worry so much about the past any more,
which couldn't, in many ways, be a good thing. Perhaps
Paula sensed that too, and probably it was the reason why
she didn't appear to approve of his returning from London
so soon.

Paula was adding now, her voice growing cold as Adrian
didn't speak, 'Of course you must do as you wish, Grant. It
is, after all, your house. It's indeed very kind of you to
allow us to live in it.'

'We don't have to go into all that, Paula.' Grant raised
laconic brows as he removed his shrewd eyes from Liza's
too expressive face, his voice, like Paula's, coolly sarcastic.

'Of course not.' Paula, as if forewarned by Grant's tone,
grew over-apologetic. Too obviously regretting introducing
such a subject, she turned gushingly to Liza. 'Perhaps you
might like a little music, dear? It can be very soothing.'

For some seconds there was complete silence while Liza
could willingly have screamed at them both. Why must
everyone imagine she needed soothing? She couldn't be
losing her reason! Or could she? Was there any way of
knowing for certain? But nothing could be worse than being
treated like a permanent invalid all the time—not at her
age!

Grant was still watching her with an almost clinical
interest. 'I'm not sure that Liza needs this particular kind
of treatment,' his tone was unexpectedly dry as his gaze
met Liza's. 'However, it is a suggestion, and maybe more
appropriate than anything else I might have in mind. Do
you have any particular composer, Liza, a favourite?'

'How would I know?' Liza stammered. 'I mean, I wish I
could remember, because I feel I liked music—still do. In
hospital, you see, I listened to a few concerts on the radio.

One of the nurses enjoyed listening too, and she tried to explain about some of the composers—Stravinsky was one, and there was something I liked by Bartók, and also Mendelssohn. Because I took to it so well she—the nurse, I mean—thought it would do no harm to concentrate a little in that direction, that it might help to bring things back naturally.'

Surprisingly Adrian moved from the window with a light laugh. 'Nothing wrong with some aspects of your immediate memory, I would say. Maybe you did enjoy our conventional composers of the past, but didn't your good nurse ever suggest something a little livelier than a Strauss waltz? Perhaps you were more promiscuous than you like to make out. How about the tarantella, or the fandango, the West Indian calypso . . .'

'Oh, no!' Liza's voice rose almost hysterically as she jumped to her feet, in no way able to cope with the rushing sense of panic that swept over her. 'Stop it!' she cried, screaming at Adrian as tears poured unheeded down her white cheeks.

Immediately Grant was beside her, holding her lightly, telling her firmly to pull herself together, then more curtly, when she protested wildly, to shut up! 'You too, Adrian,' he commanded, 'although you might have thought you were acting for the best. Didn't I tell you not to introduce any controversial subjects, at least, not for the moment, until Liza is stronger?' The curt tone was still in his voice, each note seeming to hang on the air after he had stopped speaking, and the look he flung at a suddenly anxious Adrian was not encouraging.

Liza clung to him, but his hands were hard, so obviously impatient again that the sob which rose in her throat turned into a half-gasp, but surprisingly her blind panic subsided, even if it left her feeling curiously weak, absolutely spent. 'I'm sorry,' she whispered, her face burning, her legs unsteady, 'it was when Adrian mentioned the West Indian dance, it was as if something had hit me.'

'Obviously some element there,' Paula, who had remained silent since she introduced the subject of music, broke in, an interested spectator, if sharply malicious. 'Were you ever in the South Seas, Liza?'

'I'm not sure ...' There came a roaring like waves in her ears and a wild sighing, like wind from off some pagan beach, a curious lassitude in limbs she might have dragged across silver sands. Liza put a hand to her throbbing head, hoping she wasn't becoming ill again. That would be the last straw, but it must surely be weakness of some sort that stirred these incredible fantasies which dissolved elusively before her very eyes.

Grant's teeth snapped. 'You're going to bed, Liza, so stop upsetting yourself. No one's going to hurt you or force anything from you.' He passed her his own handkerchief and she wiped her eyes, steadied by his tone. Her mind had regained control of itself, although she still felt weak and shaken—so much so that without protest she did as she was told.

Without further comment Grant escorted her upstairs, leaving her in her room after promising to send Mrs Brown to help her into bed. 'I'll see you tomorrow, my dear, before I go,' he said as he went out.

But the next morning Liza slept late because her emotional distress had not enabled her to get off to sleep easily the night before, and of course Grant was gone when she awoke.

'Mr Latham did look in,' Mrs Brown assured her, 'but he refused to disturb you. He said I was to tell you that he would see you this evening, and I'm to see you spend a quiet day.'

That, Liza thought wearily, was probably a foregone conclusion. She could scarcely do otherwise, nor did she feel really well enough for anything very energetic. Yet over the weekend she had done little else but sit in the garden watching the river and the boats that occasionally plied to and fro. Grant had shown her the grounds but chosen the easiest possible ways along the most level paths, and his hand had been beneath her arm whenever she had stumbled. Considering all this against her continuing lassitude, Liza could only conclude that her lost memory was responsible, if indirectly, and resolved somewhat helplessly that she must try and put this right.

With this in mind she ran down to the library and searched among the numerous travelogues for something on the West Indies. She found plenty, as the library was a large one, and the books ranged on a huge variety of subjects. There were several about life on almost every island in that part of the world, but nothing she could identify with any clearness. But there was the tantalising conviction she was on the right track, a feeling that at some time or another she had actually visited some of the places illustrated so vividly between the more conservative covers. Sighing, with a devastating sense of frustration, she put one of the books to one side, intending to ask Grant if she could take it to her room to pursue later. Perhaps in another mood she might remember something? Anyway, it was worth trying.

The sheer size of the library fascinated her as she explored the tightly packed shelves, and she wondered if Grant Latham was much of a reader—or was this merely a feature of the house, something he had inherited from his father along with the rest of the furnishings? In fact Liza found not merely one section but the whole of the library intriguing, and to her surprise, almost before she realised, it was time for lunch. This she shared alone with Paula.

In a cool and rather distant voice, Paula said she hoped she was feeling better. Adrian, she said, had gone out.

With an equal politeness Liza said yes, and went on quietly with her meal, realising quite clearly that Paula's disapproving demeanour must be a sort of backwash from the previous evening, but not sure what she was expected to do about it. She already felt ashamed enough of the scene she had made without seeking to excuse it. Besides, there was no guarantee that should she apologise again, or try to explain something of her confusion, that Paula would understand.

Wistfully Liza wished Adrian could have been here. While his bitterness might not be very encouraging, at least he might have diverted Paula's attention and lightened the atmosphere.

Paula, with a frown of distaste, was pushing a crisp lettuce leaf about her plate. 'By September,' she announced, 'one is tired of salads.'

Liza, who could have eaten such delectable fare all the year round, glanced at her uncertainly. 'I expect I'll appreciate all this,' she smiled, 'when I return to London and have to look after myself.'

She might have introduced a topic after Paula's own heart. Paula abandoned her lettuce leaf altogether, her eyes glittering with sharp speculation. 'You might be able to return sooner than you think,' she mused, 'as even after three days you're beginning to look decidedly better. Of course, my dear,' she continued on a note of charming hesitation, 'you know we don't mind having you, but Grant is really much too busy to have to bother with every silly little assistant who forgets her fire drill.'

As Liza blinked at her in dismay, Paula elaborated smoothly, 'Oh, I know, my dear, Grant considers I might have been at fault and you acted for the best, but one tiny little summons for the fire brigade and everything would have been dealt with quietly and efficiently through the proper channels.'

'Mr Latham...' Liza began, her face flushing brightly.

Paula could never tolerate interruptions. 'Naturally,' she stared coldly at Liza's hot cheeks, 'there are those of us who can never resist taking advantage of every situation, but Grant has really enough to do without this! I'll admit that it's chiefly for my sake he's going to all this trouble. When I asked him, perhaps inadvisedly, to do his best for you, and he eventually agreed, I didn't begin to realise it would involve so much.'

Staring at Paula, Liza felt her face grow cold. Common sense told her it couldn't all be true, what Paula said, but she felt suddenly worse than she had done when she first woke up in hospital. She knew she had been foolish about the fire; that was, at least she had realised it from one or two things she had gleaned from a reluctant Grant, but she now knew he mustn't have related all the facts. Probably, in order to save her further pain, he had concealed most of them. And Paula could be quite within her rights to be irritated by what must seem an unnecessary intrusion on her private life.

'In another week or so,' she informed Paula stiffly, 'I hope to be well enough to return to London. Even if my memory doesn't come back I don't see why it should stop me from working. The last thing I want to be is a nuisance.'

'I think you'd be very wise, my dear,' Paula looked slightly mollified. 'It would be a great relief.'

'I understand,' murmured Liza, feeling that she never would, but because of Grant she made no further protest. Why Paula should adopt this attitude she had no idea. The house belonged to Grant and was adequately staffed. Paula obviously never lifted a finger. Surely she couldn't really mind someone staying for a few days?

As if aware that her reasoning could seem regrettably devious, Paula went on to prove that she could, when she liked, be equally frank. 'I haven't a great deal of time for other people's illnesses, imaginary or otherwise, my dear. To be near someone who is sick can actually make me feel quite ill myself. Besides, I have Adrian, and am continually reminded that he needs me. Since Phoebe died he seems so very much alone.'

Which was so much Liza's own impression that she had to concede that Paula could be perceptive. 'He must have loved his wife dearly,' she replied, not really happy to be discussing Adrian's marriage, but relieved to have Paula's attention removed, if only temporarily, from herself.

'I'm not sure, dear.' Paula frowned, and Liza wondered curiously if she liked to imagine that Adrian could love no one but his mother. 'I think,' she went on with the air of one who is being very magnanimous, 'he was fond of her— she was an extremely good manager. When she was around he never had to think for himself, but to rely on anyone so completely can become a bad habit. Of course, apart from that she was a very sweet girl, and there were times when I really quite liked her. Grant was fond of her too. In fact I often thought he might have married her himself if she hadn't fallen for Adrian.'

'But she was his cousin. Grant's cousin, I mean,' Liza faltered, her heart surprisingly bleak.

'Second cousin—which is neither here nor there. Anyway, Grant is very loyal to her memory. No other woman has ever been allowed to take her place.'

A weight of misery seemed to press down on Liza from nowhere. She felt hollow and bewildered. So this was perhaps the true reason for Grant's faint coolness towards Adrian. It must have created a very uncomfortable situation when his cousin had turned him down for someone else—none other than his stepmother's son! 'Maybe,' she swallowed, suddenly aware that Paula was eyeing her oddly, 'maybe Mr Grey will meet another girl?'

'Do you know,' unexpectedly Paula smiled, 'I hope he will. Indeed I've often suggested it of late, but he refuses to listen, or if he does, he merely laughs. A thought has just occurred to me, Liza. Perhaps you could suggest it, if he ever brings up the subject. You're nearer his generation than I am, and perhaps he senses that I'm too eager that he should try anything which might help him get back to his writing. If you do get a chance it could prove one way of repaying something of what we've done for you!'

A curious expression rippled through Paula's eyes as she stared at the confused young face of the girl sitting opposite. Liza's head was bent, and her long, gleaming hair swept across her beautifully modelled cheeks, hiding momentarily the over-sensitive curve of her mouth. She didn't want to look up and meet Paula's calculating gaze again, to read in it the woman's conflicting desire to be rid of her and yet, at the same time, to have her as some sort of diversion for her son. Because this was what she appeared to be offering on a gilded plate, what she clearly considered was a delectable choice. Only to Liza it seemed more like a spoonful of nasty-tasting medicine. She was in Grant's debt, no matter what he might say about it being the other way around, but how did a girl jerk a man from months of repression? What exactly did Paula hope to achieve?

Taut with a bewildered uncertainty, Liza sat biting her full bottom lip until the slightly bitter taste told her that it bled. Yet the hurt was nothing compared with that of Paula's next words, her final, telling blow.

'I'm sure Grant, too, would be most grateful if you did something, as he always has Phoebe very much on his conscience. You see, she was out driving in his car when she was killed, and he had forgotten to tell her that the brakes were faulty. Naturally he has always blamed himself.'

CHAPTER FIVE

LIZA didn't see Adrian until after tea, when she was sitting once again by the river. She had spent the earlier part of the afternoon lying on her bed staring at the dappled shadows made by the sun on her bedroom ceiling. Her conversation with Paula had left her curiously shocked, and Paula's shattering revelations were not easy to put from her mind. Had Grant really been even indirectly responsible for Phoebe's death? Such things as faulty brakes could surely happen to anyone, but, remembering the superb condition of Grant's powerful car, Liza found it very difficult to believe he would tolerate anything less than perfect.

So convinced was she of this that a wholly incomprehensible shudder ran through her. It could, of course, have been a sheer accident, yet if it had been, why should he continue to blame himself? Paula might, on the other hand, have exaggerated, but it didn't seem possible that she had made it all up. For all she knew there was nothing to stop Liza going straight to Grant for verification.

Eventually Liza found it impossible to stay indoors any longer and sought the river. Here it was that Adrian discovered her. She wished he hadn't as she felt too distraught to talk to him, and regretted that, as a guest, she would be far from polite to remain silent. Even though Paula had asked her to, she had not intended seeking Adrian out, but apparently he had been intent on finding her.

'I wondered if you might be here,' he said, dropping down beside her on the grass. 'A penny for them?' he offered lightly, as she merely gave him a distant smile and made no reply.

76

'I was admiring the river,' she said primly, a half-truth at least, 'it's soothing.'

'At your age!' he mocked, as Grant might have done.

'I wish, Mr Grey,' she retorted stonily, 'you wouldn't insist on referring to my age as if it should be marked by some wild, abandoned activity. To be almost twenty doesn't mean one can't enjoy the less distracting things in life.'

'Touché, Miss Dean.' He glanced at her wryly. 'I suppose you're referring to my indiscreet remarks last night? Well, I'm not sure that I was on the right track, but I could have been. You may not have lived to the full, Liza, but I have a most definite feeling you haven't always been confined to the precincts of a shop.'

'There's nothing wrong with that, surely!'

'No, nothing wrong,' his eyes ran coolly over her, 'but go take a long, close look at yourself, girl. You even arouse my dormant curiosity. There's a rather wonderful flame-like quality about you which never evolved from any enclosed space. I should know, I've been around.'

'But you choose to retreat.' Unwilling to talk about herself, Liza decided to attack in turn, even if he should tell her to go jump in the river.

'So you've been poking your elegant little nose into my affairs?' His expression threw her into worse than the river!

'No, of course not.' But the flush which rose to her pale cheeks betrayed her. Adrian was like a spoiled child; he didn't politely keep such thoughts to himself, he expressed them!

He seemed more than unconvinced, but to Liza's surprise he subsided with a shrug. 'It's all right,' he grinned, 'don't panic. I imagine Paula's been getting at you. Now you'll be all softened up, ready to let me weep on your shoulder, do with you what I will in order that I might find my long-lost inspiration!'

'I'm sorry,' Liza whispered, feeling horribly embarrassed as she stared down at the water, as if searching in its un-

hurried depth for something of its undoubted tranquillity.
'I suppose I'm an open book.'

'Not you,' he muttered tersely, 'Paula. She's continually
dangling every girl she can find in front of me. She's too
blind to see it's not the answer. Can you wonder I have to
get away now and again?'

'But you come back?'

'Like a homing pigeon.' His laughter was bitter.

'Why?'

His narrowed glance was cynical. 'Perhaps I can be
miserable more comfortably here.'

'Oh . . .' Liza's face was shadowed with uncertain disapproval. What did one say to that?

'Nothing!' He read her thoughts. 'Just don't start lectur-
ing me about self-pity or, on the other hand, on how brave I
am, how uncomplaining. In fact, Liza, you might try every
permutation in the book, but if I mention I've heard them
all before it might save you trouble.'

'Oh . . .' Liza repeated again, with great originality.
There seemed not a thing left to say, every approach road
was closed. Paula should know that Adrian was impossible
to help, his ears and eyes and heart were firmly barricaded
against any kind of suggestion. And, if he enjoyed his desert
island of self-absorption, then why should anyone wear
themselves out by trying to reach him? 'If, then, we
mustn't discuss your problems,' she said truculently, 'how
about mine? I shouldn't mind anyone trying to straighten
me out. I'd simply like to get back to work as quickly as
possible.'

'A lovely young girl like you!' Adrian taunted, sneering,
his mood swinging irrationally. 'It's the last thing I would
be thinking of—in your shoes.'

Liza's face went scarlet with a smouldering indignation,
even while she tried not to take him too seriously. Paula
and he had, at least, some thoughts in common, and both
appeared to suspect she was out for all she could get! 'I
wouldn't want to take advantage of Grant's generosity,' she
retorted stiltedly.

'You're daft!' His educated voice was mockingly incredulous.

Liza managed to ignore this taunt. 'Besides,' she went on as if he had never spoken, 'I'm beginning to feel quite well, apart from my memory.'

'You ought to learn to take what the gods are prepared to offer, Liza. Small wonder they withdraw their favours when the human race is so unwilling to accept without a positive deluge of doubt.' Adrian sounded bored again.

'But not when this happens to involve expense,' Liza protested firmly. 'I don't happen to be that mercenary!'

'How do you know?'

'What do you mean?'

'What do I mean?' Adrian's eyes swung skywards, his contempt complete. 'Not a very enlightening conversation, is it, my love? You don't know what you were like in the past, but while you might not remember, instinctively you could, in coming here, be merely picking up where you left off. Grabbing the good things in life!'

Liza glared at him. 'I supposed you might be embittered, but not that much!'

The sneer ran up the side of his full mouth again; he was entirely unmoved by her indignation. 'I'm not accusing you of any crime, Liza. I've always enjoyed a lick of cream myself. So does Grant, but his worst enemy couldn't say he isn't entitled to his top of the milk, whereas mine is only by courtesy of his good nature.'

His philosophy grated. 'Surely you were left something by—Grant's father? And you must have made enough from your books ...' Liza's voice trailed off, alarmed by her own impulsive indiscretion.

'Some, but I haven't done anything since—for a year or two,' he muttered indifferently. 'So far as my mother's husband's generosity went, if that's the correct way to put it, he left me precisely nothing, but then he and Paula had only been married half a dozen years.'

'I see.'

'No reason why you should. We didn't really care for each other, the old man and I. I didn't conform to his pattern and there are no rules of inheritance for mere step-sons, especially those who step out of line. Marrying Phoebe was the best move I made, but where did that get me? Nowhere!'

Liza felt compelled somehow to gaze at him, fascinated in some inexplicable way by his lightly careless tones. He struck her as a man who had fundamentally lost interest in life, or perhaps just in his fellow men, and needed really to be pitied as well as helped. Yet she hated him when he threw insults at her and could only express her growing resentment.

'You may have problems,' she conceded, 'but I don't see how you can solve them by moping at Lynsend. Myself, I hope not to be here much longer, if only to convince you I'm not out for all I can get.'

'Well, if you're not, it must be Grant who's considering the rewards.'

'I can't think what on earth you're talking about!' Furious, Liza jumped to her feet. She wasn't sure what Adrian implied, but it sounded horrible and she refused to stay and listen. How could Paula ever imagine she could influence a man like this, when all he had done so far was insult her!

He didn't even appear distressed that he had so obviously upset her. In fact the opposite applied; he looked, if anything, smugly amused. 'It must be your red head, Liza, that makes you so touchy. That, along with a gorgeous pair of green eyes, to say nothing of a delectable figure. Has it never occurred to you that Grant could be interested in something more than your health? He shows a surprising degree of concern.'

'You make it all sound so sordid!' Liza choked. 'Grant is simply being kind.'

'Calm down, child, no use getting in a state.' Adrian slanted a speculative glance at her shaken face. 'But never say I didn't warn you. Do you actually believe a man like Grant would harbour only fatherly thoughts in his breast? He's been around, you know, even more than I have.' Swiftly, before she could move, he caught her wrist. 'Would you like me to give you a sort of brief rundown on the women he has loved and cast aside?'

Without actually hurting herself, Liza found it impossible to escape either the grasp of Adrian's vindictive fingers or the worse pain in her heart. Were all men like this? That Grant was a man of some experience she had subconsciously guessed. Maybe it was something about his mouth, occasionally the expression in his eyes, his ability to withdraw coolly from situations emotionally chaotic. At least that was how she had felt when his lips had touched hers, the one or two occasions when her ineffectual longing must have expressed itself all too clearly.

Oh, yes, there could be a lot more to him than a girl of her naïveté might suppose, but everything he had done or said had, so far, been entirely honourable. If there were smouldering fires beneath his cool exterior, Grant had done no more than let her feel the warmth of the flame.

But if what Adrian hinted at was true, how much longer would it be before Grant demanded full repayment? 'No,' she cried wildly, full of instant rejection, 'I refuse to listen! Whatever you might say, his personal life is none of my business. I don't want to hear about his—affairs.'

'You didn't think I was actually going to tell you?' Adrian mocked her over-obvious agitation. 'He's thirty-six, it would take all day.'

With painful effort, Liza dragged her arm free. 'I think you're a perfect menace!' she threw at him over her shoulder as she turned and ran towards the house, seeking the cool sanctuary of her bedroom in which to shed her suddenly anguished tears.

Of course eventually, one damp pillow later, sanity had to return, and with it the ability to control some of these near-hysterical feelings. Adrian must be extremely sick in his mind to talk the way he did, to someone who was really a stranger? It could be that Liza afforded an opportunity denied him previously. The chance to sharpen his spiteful claws on someone who could do little to hit back. Paula probably wouldn't listen, and Grant would never stand for it!

It was as if he deviously guessed at her emotional involvement with Grant and was aware that he could hurt her most at this stage, before her growing affections had time to gather the immunity of strength. And this was something that mustn't be allowed to happen. Perhaps, in a way, she could owe Adrian some gratitude as well as dislike, for drawing her attention to a danger she might not have noticed herself until it was too late!

After dinner that evening, Grant took her to the nearby village for a drink. Liza, remembering her so recently arrived-at resolution to avoid him whenever possible, was half ashamed that she didn't resist when he invited her along. At the best she managed to look doubtful, something which he easily brushed aside.

'You may not feel much like going out, but I think, for an hour, it would do you good.' His cool glance swung from Adrian to Paula, who lingered idly at the table. 'We won't wait for coffee,' he addressed his stepmother, 'Liza might like to see the countryside while there's still some light.'

'Go and get something warm to put on.' He hustled Liza into the hall, propelling her firmly, as if perfectly aware of her hesitation.

'Something warm, and only for an hour,' she twisted her head to look askance at him, her green eyes enormous, too bright. 'I don't need to be wrapped in cotton wool.'

'You're already that, my dear,' Grant's hand lay on her forearm, warm and strong, 'but you need go very slow when removing the wrappings.'

As Adrian had maintained, this man had been around! Rather frustratedly she glanced at him again. 'It must be nice to know all the answers.' She moved her small, proud head restlessly. 'Maybe some day I might!'

'Oh, I have no doubt about that, miss,' he mocked, the glance he slid over her arousing an intensity of wild rose colour, 'but until you do, it might help to have me around. I ordered a warm wrap to be included in your luggage— several heads will fall if they've forgotten to put it in, Miss Russell's included! Go and see if it's there and put it on; the evenings are growing cooler. I'll wait outside.'

'Don't you think you're being a little hasty, Grant?'

Paula's voice rose peevishly after Liza as she fled upstairs. 'The girl's been in the garden with Adrian all day. I should have thought it might have been wiser if she'd gone to bed. You really must allow me to be the better judge of some things, Grant!'

'But you must allow me a little common sense, Paula, my dear...'

Grant's words faded as Liza went out of earshot, and she didn't slow down in order to hear more. It seemed clear that Paula didn't want her going out with Grant and, for good measure, had implied that Adrian and Liza were better friends than they actually were. What did it matter? Liza shrugged, without stopping to consider why she avoided answering her own question.

The warm wrap, when she discovered it, was an expensive, silk-lined fur cape. Too luxurious, surely, for a quick drink in a local pub? Liza lingered, hesitating, but loving the feel of it, put it on. Her heavy red hair, burnished against the soft skins, looked good, and as usual her attractive reflection in the mirror gave her some faint surprise. There was also a twinge of caution. It wouldn't do to get too used to all these fine things, as the more difficult she might find it to do without them, once she was back in London.

Grant took her to a small hotel by the river, several miles upstream from Lynsend. 'You can hardly get away from the Thames in this part of the world,' he smiled, 'but slow-flowing, deep water can prove melancholy in the late evening, so I think we'll stay inside. Paula did say you'd been out all day.'

'So I heard,' Liza added wryly, 'as I ran upstairs.'

'Never mind. Paula can have a depressing effect too, and I think you need cheering, along with other things. Why do you think I've braved the commuter traffic from Town?'

She tilted her head away from him, floundering helplessly, 'I wouldn't know. I'm a new dimension for you, I suppose. You put me down as a sort of challenge.'

'You talk as though that's something I can't resist,' he said sharply.

'I don't think you can. It's become a way of life, something you can't do without. Mostly, I imagine, directed to your business interests?'

'Until recently,' he agreed.

'Why just recently?'

'Maybe one day I'll tell you.' He guided her inside, ordering drinks without asking what she wanted, and sat down beside her on the comfortable sofa he found in a secluded corner. 'One day I'll tell you,' he repeated, 'if you're still interested, but not now. We'll wait until your own emotions have time to sort themselves out.'

She was too conscious of his hands on her shoulders, removing the mink, lingering as they brushed back the silken hair which he had ruffled as he slung her cape carelessly over the back of the settee. One strand he tucked lightly behind a small pink ear. 'I can see you now,' he teased softly. 'Your hair is glorious, but not when it hides every expression.'

She fought for an even breath. 'I need to concentrate on someone else, apart from myself, I mean . . .'

'Well, according to Paula, you've had Adrian all day.' Grant's voice was back to a familiar dryness. 'When he's around no one is allowed to think about themselves. Even his silence draws the attention.'

Liza grabbed her drink, not knowing what it was, and she choked. 'You're not a particularly sensitive man, are you, Grant, not generally?'

'Stop right there, Liza.' His mouth tightened warningly. 'Too much sympathy can make people too reliant. It can act like a drug, something they find difficult to do without. It certainly wouldn't be good for Adrian. Now I don't know about you. Where you are concerned I find I'm tempted. Would you like to feel you couldn't do without me, Liza?'

His mockery had changed once more to a lighter teasing but she refused to be drawn, even if her heart beat suddenly faster. 'We were discussing Adrian,' she murmured. 'If there was always sympathy for him, none of the side effects . . .'

'It couldn't work, Liza, make no mistake. The patient

can become greedy, and the sympathiser weary, unless the recipient is truly genuine. Adrian, as I believe I've already told you, needs more astringent treatment. But not you, Liza, never you.'

'Do I detect a note of warning?'

'No. I don't ever hint, Liza. I'm simply giving you advice you'd be wise not to disregard. Learn not to melt each time you look at him. He could take advantage.'

Recalling what Paula had told her about Grant's relationship with Phoebe, and the part his carelessness had played in Phoebe's fatal accident, Liza wondered blankly how Grant could find the nerve to be so indifferent about Adrian's obvious unhappiness. Surely Grant must feel, if nothing else, a sense of responsibility?

Meeting the puzzled expression in her eyes and misunderstanding it, Grant said shortly, 'In spite of his undoubted confusion, Adrian is still a man, Liza, with all a man's weaknesses.'

'And not for me?' No sooner was it out than she would have given anything to have been able to take back such a question. Wherever had it sprung from! The last person she ever wanted was Adrian.

'You can say that again,' Grant retorted tersely, 'and keep on repeating it. If you never learn anything else, learn that! I know what's good for him.'

'And certainly not one of your shopgirls. We wouldn't be good enough!' Upset by his tone, Liza retaliated wildly. She had actually intended to explain that she had never meant to give the impression of wanting Adrian—in any way.

Grant didn't seem severely put out, his eyes merely narrowed apprehendingly on her defiant face. 'You could say that,' he drawled. 'I like to think I know what's best for my—little shopgirls.'

Liza's slender shoulders stiffened and she moved uneasily, not caring for the enigmatic set of his hard mouth. 'You'll be telling me next that I don't get my job back if I refuse to obey you!'

'The job will always be there, but I don't know about you. I may have other plans.'

'You could try telling me about them,' Liza argued, anxiously resentful, 'as they would appear to concern me.'

'I'm sorry, I can't oblige.' The glance he cast over her left no room for dissension. 'As I told you before, wait and see.'

'Maybe I haven't your patience.'

'You could be wrong about that, Liza. Mine is only limited in some respects, but you certainly haven't my experience, nor could you expect to have at your age.'

Compelled by an irrational sense of injustice, she retorted recklessly, 'How do you know? I could have forgotten things that might count towards it.'

'You could,' his cool appraisal left her in no doubt that he understood perfectly to what she was referring. 'You have an occasional flair for the outrageous which doesn't preclude such a possibility. It makes me wonder just how much your basic senses would admit and accept. The mind often wipes out that which the body refuses to, Liza.'

Well, she had asked for it! He was proving he could be as devious as she, that if she was trying to be smart, he could outmatch her, and she didn't care for what he implied one bit. It was one thing to air crazy theories, but quite another to be accused of them. Yet his voice, the low timbre of it and what he said, stirred the imagination, making her feel curiously aware of him so that her mouth felt dry and her nerves tightened electrically. If he had flung out a challenge, she was not ready yet to take it up, and could only retreat into words.

'I think you enjoy talking nonsense almost as much as I do, on occasion,' she muttered, her eyes momentarily downcast, her only defence outright retreat.

The sudden smoulder at the back of his eyes belied the indifferent shrug of his broad shoulders as he stared at her consideringly. 'Physically you might not be so able to draw back, Liza Dean,' he taunted, intent, it seemed, to punish her indiscreet tongue. 'One of these days a man might want to prove something for himself—to call your bluff. You must make sure it's me.'

Liza's fingers tightened over what could only be interpreted as a threat, and the fine stem of her glass shook as she lifted it to her lips and took another over-swift gulp. 'What is it?' she choked, meaning her drink. A subconscious effort to evade a direct answer to his comment.

'Merely your temper, I should think.' Grant's eyes were unsympathetic on her pink cheeks. 'A coward's way out. There's nothing in your drink that could be harmful to your present condition. Just soda water and lime, plus a small dash of something. Grant me some sense. I checked with your doctor.'

'I see—I mean, I'm sorry. It's probably because,' she hesitated, then added with sudden conviction, 'because I'm not used to it.'

'You remember that much?'

'All at once I do, although I can't tell you how.' A pulse beat painfully at Liza's temple and instinctively she placed the flat of her hand over it, glad they had the lounge to themselves.

He frowned sharply down at her, twisting with a quick movement of his lithe body around to face her, firmly removing her defensive fingers to soothe her hot brow himself. His eyes probed hers, forcing her to look at him, seeking to instil some of his own self-assurance.

'You know your memory might return like this, in odd flashes. Don't fight it, Liza. It won't actually hurt, you know, the brain only suggests that the pain is physical.'

Liza nodded numbly, her head drooping submissively, almost touching his shoulder, wholly responsive to his strangely gentle administrations and not wishing to see, at that moment, beyond his kindness. The room spun but righted itself almost as quickly. 'I must get used to it,' she agreed, trying to smile as she pulled away from him.

He watched her for another second before he let her go, making no further comment but ringing for another drink which he swallowed quickly. 'It might appear I'm left with the worst reactions,' he noted enigmatically, his mouth derisive. 'Maybe I ought to follow my own advice.'

In a kind of daze Liza gazed at his empty glass, the tide of comfort which his arms had brought rapidly subsiding. She did not wish to see beyond his compassion, to acknowledge her prevailing doubts. The fright she had received was already fading, replaced by another, deeper apprehension.

Adrian might have succeeded in implanting misgivings, but wasn't Grant Latham a man any girl might be proud to have around? Yet, if one were to fall in love with him, there might not be many options open. What did one usually do in such circumstances? she wondered, wishing rather desperately for a perception which wasn't hers to draw on. Grant was all too clearly not a marrying man, probably, as Paula had suggested, because of Phoebe, but nor was he a cold one. This much Liza sensed. What then did he expect from the women he took out, on whom he lavished his exclusive friendship? She flinched with bitter torment. Was it logical to suspect he would want anything at all from her, when, time and again, he had emphasised it was he who was in her debt?

'Are you having anything else?' she asked without thinking, attempting to cut off thoughts that seemed ready to suffocate her.

'No,' Grant replied, lifting an ironic eyebrow at her, 'I'm driving, remember. Besides, I think you've been out long enough.' Gathering her cape from behind her, he slipped it smoothly around her silken shoulders. 'I have to return to Town tomorrow, unfortunately, but I hope to be back at the weekend. Something has cropped up and I'm afraid there's no possible way I can get out of it. You know there's a Doctor Sutherland coming down tomorrow to continue your treatment. You must endeavour to be in.'

'Of course.' Liza flushed, not appreciating Grant's sudden curtness. 'Where else would I be?'

This doctor, an experienced psychiatrist who specialised in amnesia, had his own private clinic and, imagining the size of his fees, she trembled. To protest, she knew from past skirmishes, would only arouse Grant's wrath, and so she stayed silent, unaware that her anxious expression gave away everything that passed through her head.

They went back through Cookham, but the red-brick cottages which Liza had admired an hour ago were now shadowed in darkness although here and there lights flickered and people still lingered outside, enjoying their doorsteps on an Indian Summer night.

For no good reason, Liza sighed, and hearing it Grant said softly, as if regretting his former abruptness, 'If you like, when I return on Saturday we can go on the river. If you think you'll enjoy it, it might be something to look forward to.'

'I'm not sure.' Liza clenched her small fists, clutching instinctively at any area where she might reasonably defy him. Only a fool would jump headlong into a situation that even theoretically might prove more than she could cope with! A day out such as he suggested could spell danger, although many would merely laugh and tell her she was being quite stupid even to suspect it.

Grant obviously considered her stupid to hesitate. 'You can't be scared of the river,' he teased lightly, to her surprise suddenly swinging the car off the road, a few yards down a winding track to within a few feet of it.

'Look,' he smiled, nodding towards the slow-flowing water that glinted darkly beneath the light of a rising moon, 'you can see there's nothing there to be frightened of.'

'It seems I'm afraid of more things than I ever imagined,' Liza retorted shakily, scarcely realising that they had stopped, that Grant had pulled on his brakes and switched off the engine. The sight of the wide stretch of water, the small eddying waves tinted white in the moonlight as they spilt upon the shore, woke that nameless apprehension within her, filling her with such apparent agitation that Grant, after a frowning glance at her paling face, reached out and drew her close.

This time he refused to take her seriously. 'You've simply got an outsize imagination.' His eyes probed hers, daring her to dispute it. 'I must have tried the wrong therapy in the hotel,' he said, and put a gentle hand beneath her chin, bending his head as he spoke, softly kissing her.

His mouth was warm against hers and the strange flicker of sensation which Liza had known when he had kissed her before ran through her. There also returned her barely suppressed longing to be held closer, along with her former conviction that Grant's conscience was forcing him to offer this kind of friendship. As if he guessed at her need for more personal contact than her peculiarly relationless state allowed, and drove himself to supply it.

In spite of her misgivings there was no resisting him, but she tried too desperately to hold herself stiffly, even when she felt the familiar tremors starting within her as his arms encircled her completely and his lips moved, feather-light, to her brow.

'Something for you to think about, along with our trip down the river.' She could feel his hard mouth quirk to a smile, and almost see the laughter in his eyes as his fingers traced the tense lines of her face.

'I think I must concentrate on the things that matter,' she murmured in an attempt to reject his suggestion, her own eyes wide with a tremulous unhappiness.

'You're still too anxious about yourself, aren't you, Liza? You won't even try to trust me.'

'It's not that,' her hands were suddenly clinging to him, 'you can't imagine what it's like, this blank wall I'm continually faced with! Each morning I wake and think it's sure to be gone and everything will be all right, but it never is. The thing is, it seems to get harder instead of easier, as could be the case, I suppose, with some afflictions.'

'It won't last for ever.'

'So you keep on telling me, and I'm sorry to keep on complaining . . .'

'Never that,' his voice was curt. 'I recognise that it must help a lot to be able to talk. In fact it could be a necessity, and that's what I'm here for, to listen.'

Her words were strangled against the strong column of his throat. 'I can't take advantage of that.'

'Maybe I'm enjoying it,' his mouth moved softly against her ear, where he swept back the heavy hair. 'Man is a universally selfish creature, Liza. He rarely does anything without drawing some reward, a certain amount of pleasure.'

For a long moment her breath stalled as she felt the pressure of his mouth deepen on her warm skin, awakening a kind of torment as the way he held her allowed no response, only he deriving any satisfaction, at the expense of her racing pulse, her natural instincts which it seemed must be denied. 'I think I must go back to London,' she choked, her heart throbbing wildly, 'I must have a look round my flat.'

'We'll talk about it at the weekend,' he murmured, as if not paying a great deal of attention.

His apparent indifference helped. She was able to pull an inch or two away from him, anger slight but giving her some necessary strength. 'I imagine with this show of affection you're trying to prove I'm as normal as anyone?'

'If you like,' his tone was guarded, 'but if so, there could be hazards. When your memory returns, Liza, you could remember you hated the sight of me. Perhaps I'm trying to change that impression while I have the chance.'

'But,' her voice was tentatively startled, 'I didn't even know you.'

'No, you could say that, although I had seen you.'

'You mean,' frowning, she considered, 'you recognise a lot of your employees by sight, rather like ...' suddenly, more cheerfully, she giggled, 'I was reading of a farmer who could recognise every one of his hundreds of sheep individually.'

She saw his wry grin through the dim light. 'I should advise you not to let Miss Russell hear you say that! Besides, I'm afraid so far as I'm concerned it's far from true, but I do know a certain few.'

'All who count.' Liza copied something of his own dryness. 'Remember how I visualised a small establishment with you, more or less, behind your own counter. You must have thought me incredibly stupid!'

He shook her slightly. 'One day you might discover you're a terrible little snob, Liza Dean. I spent weeks behind my own counters, as you put it, when I was younger.

Now, if I don't it's because I haven't the time any more, but how were you to know?'

She chose to ignore much of what he said. 'There are those who would say I should have guessed the truth simply by looking at you.'

'Then in a way, it's perhaps as well you didn't.' His voice was coolly contained again as he put her firmly from him. 'Your imagination is too vivid as it is. This way, at least, we've come to know each other.'

'You might know me, but not me you!' She felt too suddenly isolated when he released her, and stammered stupidly as her lighter mood departed.

He laughed as he turned from her, switching on the ignition. 'I don't know what that's supposed to mean,' he teased, 'but it does tell me you never went to school. Am I such an enigma, Liza?'

'No—yes . . .' Not gone to school? The pain was gnawing at her again, but she hid it successfully. Leave it to the psychiatrist, he might know all the answers! 'I guess the enigma is me,' she faltered, her eyes despairingly following the white line of the road, caught unwavering in their headlights.

'So you like to think. All women love a mystery, Liza, you could simply be running true to form.'

The coldness was back, jarring, a douche of cold water, and she drew a swiftly bracing breath. 'If I know nothing else,' she retorted bleakly, 'I know that sometimes I hate you. You're worse than Adrian. At least one knows where one is with him. He doesn't pretend to be sympathetic!'

Grant could have been infuriated, but he merely shrugged. 'That's why I think he could be good for you, in reasonable doses. He'll take your mind off yourself, help you face up to the harsher realities of life. As a small child you could have been over-fond of fairy tales.'

'It's nice to know.' Liza's reply was sober, a dull acceptance, as exhaustion took over. She could owe him an apology, but she decided to leave it. 'It might be better for everyone if I were to go.'

The glance he slung at her didn't claim to be anything

less than threatening, making not one single allowance for her obviously distraught frame of mind. 'Don't ever consider doing that,' he commanded. 'Unless you're quite prepared to face my fury, don't even think of leaving here without telling me!'

CHAPTER SIX

TIME until Saturday dragged so much that Liza grew a little desperate and almost welcomed Adrian's attention when he chose to seek her out. Her indifference to him didn't change on closer acquaintance, but she found herself listening with increasing fascination whenever he talked about his work. As Grant and Paula had both remarked that he could never be persuaded to so much as mention it, it surprised Liza when he began to discuss it quite freely with her. Not that she was able to do much more than listen, but occasionally she asked a few questions. These must have been the right sort, as Adrian usually answered with apparent willingness, even an eagerness, that encouraged Liza to think that in some ways he was almost as lost as she was herself. To become absorbed in Adrian's troubles seemed one way of forgetting her own, one way to stop her mind centring exclusively on another man.

Later in the week Adrian said: 'We might go out this afternoon and have tea somewhere. If you can escape your jailors?'

Liza smiled ruefully while she accepted his invitation, the sarcastic indifference in his voice she tried to ignore. Mrs Brown watched over her like a hawk, Liza suspected on Grant's instructions. Mrs Brown had related to Liza how she had worked as a nursing auxiliary during the war, but whatever her medical qualifications, Liza had little doubt of her ability as a watchdog, although neither that nor a jailor seemed a very appreciative way of describing the woman's kindly concern.

To herself Liza could have confessed she was often

grateful to have Mrs Brown around, as her memory did, in fact, appear to be returning in small, peculiar flashes. Nothing dramatic, but at times she felt nervous, for the messages as yet were not nearly concrete enough to form clear pictures, to do anything much but endue a feeling of strain.

All such fears, of course, were to be controlled, especially to be hidden from Adrian's jaundiced eyes, so she smiled and said she would like very much to have tea with him, providing they were not too late in coming home.

Adrian took her to Windsor, and for a while they wandered around the town, which was very attractive in the drowsing warmth of the afternoon. He showed her the Castle, that had been built, he said, on a site chosen by William the Conqueror. It had first become a royal residence in the reign of Henry the First, and there were additions dating from that time until the reign of Queen Victoria. Much of the Castle visible from the river was built after 1824. The Lower Ward, containing St George's Chapel, was now the burial place of royalty.

'You appear to know a great deal about it,' Liza remarked, forced to admit that owing to the state of her memory, she knew very little, although she could vaguely recall the Queen.

'I should,' Adrian smiled dryly, 'as I've mostly lived in these parts.'

The huge Castle took all Liza's attention and she listened eagerly as he explained the Middle Ward, which contained the famous Round Tower, and the Upper Ward where the state apartments were to be found, as well as the Sovereign's private apartments. She could scarcely visualise the Great Park with its thousands of acres. It all seemed so vast, the wonderful architecture, the land—so much responsibility. All to be looked after, handed down to posterity. This, with the royal family, the inheritance of a nation.

'I'm thinking of setting my next book locally,' Adrian interrupted her marvelling thoughts with this startling, if apparently idle, announcement. 'I shan't involve Her Majesty, of course, or the Castle,' he grinned, misreading her surprised expression.

'No,' murmured Liza, 'of course not.' She ought to have said more, but felt stunned, while aware that she should have been ready with enthusiastic encouragement in case he should change his mind. Should Paula ever hear of such feeble a reaction she would be furious!

Liza, however, need not have worried. Her startled silence seemed no deterrent. 'I've been working out the general outlines of my plot this morning,' Adrian continued, adding lightly, 'I've more or less finalised it as we've walked this afternoon. Something you might find hard to believe, Liza, but you've a wonderfully helpful aura around you, something I never thought to find again.'

Still she couldn't find an intelligent remark, some part of her unwilling to fill this mystic rôle, to accept that she could influence him in any way. To her relief he changed the subject while she searched for a reply that might satisfy them both and, as he talked of other things, her eyes lingered on the many small craft on the river, her thoughts turning with no small longing to the weekend, when Grant had promised to take her out himself.

Adrian had raised his arm and was pointing to Eton on its north bank, with its famous school, founded in 1440, and as they strolled back around Windsor Liza found much to admire wherever she looked. Adrian, she realised, was making sure she didn't miss a thing.

'You've a lot to learn,' he teased softly, when she thanked him. 'We're a couple of lame ducks, and can probably help each other.'

'Lame ducks? Oh, I see.' Liza smiled back at him as he prepared to order tea in a small but delightful restaurant. She wasn't sure she enjoyed his joke. It had rather too much truth in it to be amusing!

'Never mind,' he shrugged, watching her expressive face, 'Paula approves, and even Grant seems tolerant, so as providence appears to shine on us we may as well enjoy ourselves. The only snag might be Saturday.'

'Saturday?'

'When Grant has hinted he doesn't want me around,'

Did Grant hint? Liza wondered. She felt uncomfortable

beneath Adrian's curiously raised eyebrows. 'He's taking me on the river,' she faltered. 'Of course there's nothing definite, he only suggested it. He may not be free. This week, as you know, he's busy.'

'But still finds time to ring you every evening. So, you could almost take Saturday for granted. He might not want me, but if you did, I would be willing to risk his wrath and go along.' With the air of a man bent on experimenting, Adrian considered her tentatively for a few minutes before covering her fingers reassuringly with his. He didn't appear to wonder why she didn't answer, obviously taking her agreement for granted.

For the rest of the week Liza hoped Adrian would forget about it. Come to that, she hoped Grant would too, because while she was somehow longing to see him she shared no such enthusiasm for the river. Grant kept a medium-sized boat, but usually only used it when he took a long holiday. Adrian had mentioned that Grant had a fondness for the Greek islands and the West Indies, and would occasionally spend up to a couple of months in the Caribbean.

As always when Liza thought of deep water, especially in far-off lands, she shuddered, knowing an inexplicable apprehension, a need to suppress a wild hysteria. On Saturday she was aware that Grant might have small patience with this continuing nervousness, but if Adrian wasn't there she might cope more easily with Grant's arid remarks. How impossible to make Grant understand that water brought a kind of nameless terror she just couldn't shake off.

On Saturday morning, from her bedroom window, she saw Grant drive up to the front door and found she couldn't contain herself to wait patiently until he sought her out, until he had perhaps spoken to his family. He looked so tall and dark, so incredibly handsome as he stood there beside his car, that her breath caught unevenly in her throat and she found herself almost shaking. Her heart quickened excitedly and some of the fear that was always with her left, his mere presence bringing renewed confidence, a sure knowledge that all would be well.

'You're looking better, I think.' Grant's eyes went critically over her as she ran from the house, out on to the red-gravelled drive to meet him. 'What have you been doing with yourself?' he smiled.

'Waiting for you,' she laughed, quite beautifully, her glinting hair dancing and her wide, thickly lashed eyes lit like a pair of sparkling emeralds. She was conscious that his hands went out to her arms, holding her contemplatively, his clasp lighter than his expression flooding her with incredible longing, so that she forgot how she had almost hated him.

'I intended coming last night,' he said, a significant satisfaction edging his voice as she trembled visibly, 'but I was held up. It didn't seem sensible to return here at midnight, much as I wanted to.'

Liza had a feeling he was merely making conversation, that he had other matters besides herself on his mind. She could tell by the way his mouth went taut when he finished speaking. Ruefully she drew away from him as his hands left her. The atmosphere had changed in a flash and it was difficult to know why. His dark face gave nothing away, there was merely a kind of watchful indifference. Bewildered, as he spun around, she followed him into the house.

He had, as usual, some work to complete, some telephone calls to make, and it was after lunch before they left for the promised trip on the river. Liza hadn't seen Adrian all morning, but much as she would have liked to, her conscience wouldn't allow her to forget.

'Adrian said he wouldn't mind coming with us this afternoon,' she began limply.

Grant spared her only one sharp glance. He wore a pair of light linen slacks with a blue shirt, a little lighter than his eyes, with a thick, serviceable pullover slung around his shoulders. In it he still looked elegant but at the same time tough, masculine enough to make any girl's heart miss a beat. 'No way,' he replied emphatically, leaving her in no doubt that he wouldn't change his mind. 'Besides, he isn't even around.'

'I told you before, he and Mrs Latham are lunching with

friends, but he won't be late in coming back. Well, that's
what he told Mrs Brown.'

'We could hang around all day—I happen to know
Adrian. He has no idea of time and we're late enough as it
is. Come on.' Firmly he handed her on to the boat, choosing
to ignore the note of uncertainty in her voice. 'Adrian, at
close quarters for several hours, is more than I can stomach
after a hard week in London.'

Relief swam through Liza as the responsibility of such a
decision was taken decisively from her. Thankfully she
perched on the first thing she found on deck. Adrian
couldn't accuse her of not trying, anyway. He had gone out
of his way during the past few days to be nice to her and
she hoped he wouldn't be too cross about this afternoon.
Only she had wanted Grant to herself, although she didn't
expect Grant to feel the same way.

'Don't look so glum,' Grant shot her a mocking glance
across his shoulder as the boat began to move, not fooled for
a minute by her blank expression. 'You'll find you can't run
with the hare and hunt with the hounds, Liza.'

'You being one of the hunters?' She met his cool gaze
with more than a hint of resistance.

'Well, you do sometimes remind me of some small wild
creature, Liza, but I wasn't actually putting you in that
position. It was simply because you appear to excel occasionally in the art of evasion. You're not something I have
any desire to eat or kill. I can think of a much more satisfactory fate for you.'

'Oh!' There seemed nothing she could find to say to
that, and she knew again the futility of trying to deceive
him. But he was too busy right then to provoke her further,
and she turned her face from him to study the river.

It was a beautiful late summer afternoon, with the sun
just warm enough to be comfortable and the slight breeze
soothing and fragrant with the scent of flowers, of ripening
grasses and autumn fruits from the gardens and fields which
swept down to the water. An afternoon when surely, in such
a setting, it should be possible to relax completely.

Yet Liza was aware that even with Grant's protective

warmth so near her she was still nervous, still wary, in some confusing way, of the water. Now, the motion of the boat seemed to add to this, and the gentle swing of the deck beneath her feet was mentally hurtful. Bewildered, she stared around her. The ketch, an ocean-going one, was kept in the boathouse so she hadn't seen it until today. It was smart, she conceded, liking its slim lines, the impression of speed about its bows, its air of spaciousness. One part of her delighted in it, an appreciative excitement rising involuntarily, an ever-spreading pleasure not to be resisted. Why then should she have these other feelings of what almost amounted to repulsion, an indescribable desire to jump overboard, to swim frantically ashore?

As always she sought to hide and conquer her irrational emotions by turning to Grant. He was so much stronger than she was, so much in control of everything he said and did that even to gaze on him steadied her leaping nerves considerably. She never ceased to marvel at his obvious expertise, how organised he was in most things. At Lynsend he kept staff but used it economically. The man who drove his car knew as much about boats, and he had had everything ready for them. Mrs Brown was cook-housekeeper, apparently with nursing experience, and did all the household shopping. The young gardener also worked indoors and could turn his hand to almost anything.

Grant's man, however, hadn't come with them today. 'I've given John the afternoon off,' he grinned, coming to lounge beside her, 'so if I need any help you'd better be prepared to make yourself available.'

'Of course,' Liza replied automatically, as he hauled her to her feet and showed them around.

'You don't seem very surprised by any of it,' he remarked shrewdly, watching her too closely as they returned.

'Should I be?' she asked tautly, not wanting him to know that she had been asking herself the same question. 'Possibly I might have done a little sailing, but how would I know?'

'Never mind.' It seemed he didn't want to spend the afternoon delving into her mysterious past any more than she did. 'You're looking particularly attractive in what you're wearing,' his eyes roved over her, the sleekly fitting blue jeans which clung to her slender hips, the simple white cotton top, and she flushed beneath his lingering scrutiny. 'At least you haven't forgotten how to do that,' he remarked enigmatically.

She wasn't sure what he meant, nor did she wonder overmuch as she sought to divert him with the first thing to enter her head. 'Yesterday Adrian took me to Windsor, and told me he's completed the first page of a new book, and has more or less roughed out the first stages of his plot.'

'You're joking!'

'He said so.'

Grant's eyebrows rose, a sceptical stare, to be followed by a swift frown. 'It must be sheer coincidence. It's too soon.'

'Too soon for what?'

'For you to have anything, even indirectly, to do with it. You shouldn't have the responsibility thrust on you. Nor should you flatter yourself, my dear.'

'You couldn't call it credit!' She had not meant to put it like that, to so much as suggest she had anything more than a passing interest in the matter, but Grant's dryness stung. Which was perhaps no excuse for seeking to antagonise him, but it seemed she must put some impenetrable distance between them. If her memory was not functioning properly maybe an instinctive sense of self-preservation was working overtime?

She had never seen him really angry, not with her, but now she thought he could be! There was a coolness in the depth of his blue eyes that froze her still. 'You would love to think it was like that, wouldn't you, Liza? A woman must always be necessary to someone, essential. They're never happy until they've wormed their way into such a position. Even you, at the moment a nonentity, floating in space.'

That hurt, as she suspected it was meant to, and she could only gasp, 'I never meant it like that, and you must know I didn't! Your low opinion of women is another thing.'

He ignored the last bit. 'But you sound as if you were personally involved, or as if you would like to be.'

'I'm not—I don't,' Liza stumbled. 'He talks to me and I listen, only that, but perhaps this is what he's lacked. You've all been so busy advising, telling him where he's made his mistakes; why he shouldn't brood so much; how he must continue with his career.'

'Spare me the dramatics, my dear.' Grant's mouth clamped tight. 'I could tell you quite ruthlessly that you don't know what you're talking about, but it might be sufficient to warn you to take care. If I'd known he was at home I'd never have brought you here.'

His strong words hurt. Did he trust her no more than she trusted him? Yet for all his open contempt, she was ashamed of such thoughts as soon as they entered her head.

She heard him saying almost grimly, his eyes fixed broodingly on the passionate curve of her mouth, 'You're too vulnerable, Liza. Too . . .' he hesitated, 'a lot of things, once you learn to let go. You could well be lost on the tide of your own emotions, but it's got to be with a man who won't take advantage, one who knows what he's doing. Not someone like Adrian who would undoubtedly use you merely to further his own ends.'

Which seemed a bit hard on Adrian, especially as Grant himself must have been the cause of a lot of Adrian's un-happiness. But she couldn't suddenly bear that Grant should be looking at her with such brutal dislike, as if she was the only one at fault! What had happened to their glorious afternoon? She couldn't let Adrian spoil it!

'Please, Grant,' she whispered, feeling near to tears, 'do we have to quarrel?'

'No,' he replied abruptly. 'Nor do we have to discuss Adrian at all, but remember you started it! I suggest we talk about other things. Well,' he smiled, as she waited, 'there's always the river.'

'Fine,' she laughed, a teasing glint replacing tears, 'but unless you intend running aground, I think you'd better get back to your wheel. I've a mind myself, sir, to go below to the trireme to brew a cup of strong tea.'

For a moment he did not move, then he leaned towards her, noticeably speculative. 'A trireme is a galley, if of a different kind.' His fingers tilted her chin, an odd light in his eyes. 'Once I met a man who called it that, but I haven't heard it in a long time. Where did you?'

'I don't know,' she blinked, staring up at him, faintly confused, as if she was trying to see herself, not him. 'I feel I know something about sailing, but not on rivers. Maybe at sea, where you'd be rapping out orders, would you not, slackening and tightening ropes. Having trouble with the sail until I arrived to give you a hand ...'

'How would you know?' His eyes glittered as they scanned her bewildered face. 'And I never have trouble with my sail, Liza. The elements, now, that's a different thing.'

'How would you know?' His eyes glittered as they scanned her bewildered face, 'And I never have trouble with my sail, Liza. The elements, now, that's a different thing.'

'How would you know?' His eyes glittered as they scanning her bewildered face, 'And I never have trouble with my sail, Liza. The elements, now, that's a different thing.'

picious, I mean. Because I do seem to know. I seemed to recognise the feel of the deck beneath my feet and imagined I was at sea. There was the excitement of the wind catching the sail, the long waves running white, sparkling where the sun touched them to emerald, and you said ...' Acutely embarrassed of a sudden, she broke off, frowning away from him.

'What did I say? That wasn't around these shores, surely.'

'I can't remember.' There was pain in her voice, the resentment and hopelessness of long denial. 'Why can't I, Grant?' Her eyes implored him, and his hand shifted to her waist, but only to give her a slight push.

There was a mocking twist to his sudden smile. 'Go down to the galley, girl, and prepare that tea. It could be that in boats we might find a lot of answers, but I wouldn't worry overmuch about something which might not even be relevant. You've been reading a lot since your accident.'

'You could be right,' gratitude gleamed. 'I don't particularly want to remember anything, Grant. It hurts.'

'I know that,' suddenly he was very cool, 'and for this afternoon I entirely agree. I intend, as I told you before, to relax. So must you. If your memory starts playing up again we'll forget it.'

Below in the galley everything was spotless, beautifully appointed, glittering with polish. Liza found all she required easily, and managed somehow to ignore the message transmitted from hands which seemed naturally to know exactly what to do. She found two workmanlike mugs and, filling them full, carried them back on deck, passing one carefully to a preoccupied navigator. Taking her own, she sat down a short distance away, turned her eyes from his handsome dark face and again watched the river.

They appeared to be moving slowly up a long stretch of it, having left Cookham and Bourne End behind, and were approaching Marlow Lock. Grant, she was not surprised to learn, was quite an authority on the workings of the river, and pointed out most places of interest as they went along. The locks and weirs in particular intrigued Liza, and she thought the setting at Marlow, with its wonderful beech-woods, quite beautiful.

'The Thames,' Grant told her, 'is just over two hundred miles long. The Mississippi is two thousand five hundred and sixty, but the Thames can claim to be a model river in many ways. There are around forty-five lock sites with associated weirs, all of which far too many people take for granted, and few are able to say clearly why they exist or how they work. A lot of locks are mechanical now,' he added. 'Usually the lock-keeper can do most of the work from his office by pressing buttons on a panel—open gates, close gates, stop gates, and so on. There's no necessity for him to leave his hut at all, unless it's to collect fees.'

'You ought to write a book about it,' Liza suggested, impressed by such a detailed fund of knowledge.

Wryly he shook his head. 'I leave that to the experts, whom I enjoy reading. It would be too much to suppose no one has ever put pen to paper. Think of all the famous places the Thames flows through. The river at Oxford, Windsor and Westminster, London City. Then there's Shakespeare and Wren, Francis Drake and Raleigh, the *Mayflower* and the *Golden Hind*. More might only confuse you, Liza, but the list is almost unending.'

As they waited to get through Marlow Lock he told her some more, as if partly determined to keep her thoughts from herself. 'The river rises in the Cotswolds and follows a tranquil but somewhat devious course through seven counties. For instance, by river from Oxford to Teddington is ninety-two miles, but as the crow flies only forty-two.' And once past Marlow, he said, 'Cookham and the fantastic Cliveden Woods take a lot of beating, but this is my favourite part of the Thames.'

'I noticed you didn't go down the river.' Liza gazed ruefully at her mug, her tea long grown cold.

'I didn't,' he agreed, slanting her a mocking look, 'but what would have been the use, when you've only just been there with Adrian?'

Later, much later, when it was almost dark they returned. Grant dropped anchor in a deep cove, sheltered by the beechwoods on the high banks where many of the branches dipped into the water, about a mile from Lynsend. 'We can have dinner in peace,' he smiled, 'if you'll be a good girl and help me to cook it.'

Down below space was somewhat limited with two of them moving about in the galley, but they managed. 'If you weren't so slim it might be awkward,' he looked rather lazily down at her, exploring her warmly tinted face as she turned their steaks. 'You appear to be a very good cook, Liza,' he remarked conversationally. 'I might just happen to borrow you from the shop when I go abroad again. You seem to be extremely versatile.'

She gripped the fork in her hand so tightly that it hurt her still tender fingers, as she made an effort not to turn and look at him, knowing he would immediately read in her face a tremulous excitement. Even to suggest going with him on a trip was enough to arouse that!

She must take good care that he didn't realise it, but he was not a man from whom it was easy to hide things. He must feel her slight quiver as he stood behind her, letting his arms slide unerringly around her narrow waist as he drew her protectively back against him, but his expression was inscrutable. 'You don't have to convince me,' she spluttered, her pulses leaping madly as she felt every taut muscle of his hard body.

He merely laughed as he pulled the neck of her cotton top to one side, the slight roughness of his chin catching her cheek as he bent his head to kiss the soft white skin of her shoulder. 'Don't worry,' he laughed gently as he felt her stiffen and pull away warily, 'I'm too ravenous to think seriously of delaying your good work, although I expect you realise there's more than one kind of hunger?'

She swallowed, helpless in the grip of intense emotion, the glance she threw at him wide and unguarded. Her voice was low. 'I'd be a bit of a fool if I didn't, but you rather frighten me, Grant. I don't have your sophistication.'

'How do you know?'

Her body curved sideways, and she escaped his lingering hold to rescue the steak. 'Somehow that doesn't sound flattering.'

His eyes seemed to flash sceptically. 'Sometimes I find myself wondering. Have you ever been abroad, Liza? Out in the South Seas time doesn't seem to matter as it does here. Have you ever made love between courses, my small puritan?'

Now she knew he was deliberately trying to shock, and once in control of her racing nerves, she said, 'No,' so emphatically as to raise his dark eyebrows.

'I thought not.' His laughter was low and mocking as he let her go. 'Now don't panic. I happen to have no fondness for burnt steak—or uncertain young redheads.'

Why could she subdue everything but a quickening excitement! Hastily she involved herself in the crisping of some potatoes, yet couldn't refrain from exclaiming angrily, 'You wouldn't be trying to hide the fact that you've been around?'

His white teeth glinted. 'It's a man's prerogative, surely, little one.'

'And not a woman's?' He had a nerve!

'That's about the way of it, Liza.'

'Oh!' The force with which she slapped a piece of

sizzling steak on his plate expressed all she left unsaid. 'You'd better have this now,' she muttered, not noticeably graceful, 'otherwise it will be ruined, along with your appetite.'

They drank their coffee on deck much later, by the light of a moon that played hide and seek among slow-moving fragments of feathered cloud. 'Wind tomorrow, most probably,' Grant grunted, glancing wryly at the sky.

Liza nodded. Their meal, and the bottle of light wine they had shared, had been good, and she had found herself enjoying it enormously. Now she felt replete, strangely at peace, as she sat down once more on the cushioned seat against the bulkhead, the half-smile of contentment on her expressive face apparently prompting him to say, 'You seem to have enjoyed your day, copper-top?'

'Yes.' She liked the companionable way he lounged beside her, his long legs dwarfing her slim limbs as he stretched lazily against her across the mattress. She had the most soothing feeling of being suspended between two worlds, neither of which she was very familiar with. A sort of floating in the kind of space to be seen above them, beyond the stars.

'What are you thinking about?' he asked idly, when she added no more to her brief utterance. 'Surely not the general scenery?'

'What else?' she prevaricated, unable to confess that it was his image that possessed her mind, the stars in the heavens merely incidental. But startled by the sudden intensity of her thoughts, she edged back a little, away from him, to drink defensively of her coffee, her fingers taut, the knuckles white.

'You could say me,' he teased lightly, removing her empty cup and placing it firmly out of reach. 'You don't have to alter the shape of it,' he drawled, 'I'm quite satisfied with the way it is. Do you ever,' he persisted, his mouth curving with amusement, 'think about me?'

'Yes.' Liza didn't try to deny it, but her voice was guarded, and she kept her face protectively in the shadows.

'It would surely be very strange if you never crossed my mind.'

His eyes slipped over her downbent head, the heavy, evasive sweep of her lashes. 'But if I asked in exactly what way, what would you say?'

She gave him a little burning glance, not caring to be cornered in this manner. 'With gratitude, I suppose,' she answered resentfully, her slender hands clasping. Never would he wring from her more than that!

He shrugged his wide shoulders, darkness veiling his eyes. 'So my curiosity must remain unsatisfied. If I wish for more satisfactory answers I must discover them myself?'

'You could be disappointed,' she warned very quickly, finding it suddenly necessary to draw on the last remaining wits she had. She knew a great urge to retreat, but refused to pander to such weakness, yet found the effort to stay where she was almost intolerable.

'What if I were willing to take the risk?'

It was too much, such barefaced provocation. Breathless, Liza started to her feet, only to find his hand closing on her shoulder. 'You thinking of going somewhere?' His smile was taunting.

'I don't know,' she whispered, making the mistake of halting her immediate flight as his arm, finely controlling, drew her steadily closer. She could feel his heart beating against hers, the roughness of his suntanned skin where his shirt lay carelessly open over his broad chest, and within her the desire to resist him was fast fading. She stared into his decisive face, not realising how the flickering moonlight illuminated her own, her uncertain thoughts, all too clearly.

With his forefinger Grant traced the beating pulse in her throat. 'You don't have to take everything so seriously.'

'Don't do that!' Almost pleadingly she tried to jerk away, her skin throbbing at his touch, her senses stirred by his low, intimate tone.

'Poor Liza,' his voice mocked, and he didn't allow her another inch as he held her against him. 'Do you imagine I would ever hurt you? You enjoyed the wine, didn't you, that we drank at dinner, even if to begin with you viewed it with unmistakable apprehension? Well, I suggest you learn to enjoy an interlude such as this in exactly the same way. Such knowledge, when you're out again in the world, could only be useful.'

Flickers of fright showed in her face. What he said was outrageous! 'How to become a lover in six easy lessons?' she flung back at him, a flare of quick temper sweeping aside despair.

'You said that, Miss Dean,' he said pleasantly, his hand shaping her head, uncaring, it seemed, of her indignation as his mouth came down with a forceful insistence.

On those other occasions he had been gentle with her, and so he was, in a way, this evening. If there was a coiled strength about him he kept it well in check, and if her lips parted beneath his it was of their own accord, as he held her only lightly. So much more experienced than she was, he didn't press home any natural advantage, seeming content to wait until she melted against him as the blood began to pound through her veins. Without even trying he aroused emotions she found difficult to control, nor did she seem to want to after the first few tormenting seconds. While his arms and lips were gentle it was suddenly not enough. Yet afterwards, Liza could never understand how she'd been shameless enough to whisper, 'Kiss me properly, please, Grant!'

His eyes, swiftly narrowed, roved her tormented face. Roughly he asked, not sparing her now, 'Would you risk it?'

'Try me,' she spoke faintly, an odd note of desperation in her voice, driven beyond herself, yet she marvelled that it should be so. Emotion such as she felt couldn't be wrong, and the need to seek a closer fulfilment was overwhelming. She made a convulsive little movement, and suddenly, very urgently, he was thrusting his hands along the fragile line of her jaw, through her tumbled hair, dragging her to him. As his mouth met hers again, it was like a million stars exploding. His lips were hard and possessive against hers and her mouth hurt as he crushed it so that his breath mingled with her own. Between them the quickening white fire of desire developed into consuming passion, a flare of feeling so vivid as to be frightening. Never had Liza imagined anything could be like this!

'Grant!' his name was torn from her, subdued yet urgent as she attempted to evade him. She succeeded, a mere fraction.

He smiled, without noticeable mirth, as her eyes, dark pools of anguished pleading, met his. 'Don't pretend to be surprised, Liza,' he ran a finger over her bruised mouth. 'You asked me to, and I thought I was doing rather well, so why complain? And don't tell me you didn't enjoy it!'

She hated him then—when he spoke to her like that. If she was utterly devastated, maybe, as he implied, it was partly her own fault, but need he have used such a sensual technique? Such controlled savagery was beyond her comprehension. She wanted nothing more than to be able to hit him, and it wasn't easy to divert such violent thoughts into more civilised channels. 'I'm not complaining,' the moonlight etched the intensity of tears, outlining her inner agitation. 'I suppose I've been extremely stupid.'

'Darling,' again Grant drew her closer, disregarding a swiftly indrawn breath, and held her tightly. Her sensitive face was shadowed, her heart racing beneath his hand with over-excited emotion, ever-widening waves of searing sweetness. All this he took in in one fully encompassing glance, but it seemed he had exhausted his supply of indulgence. 'Stop fighting a battle,' he advised, 'you never had any chance of surviving anyway.'

It was as if her feeble protest had never been, and this time when he kissed her she didn't try to deny him. Her arms went up around his neck and clung, wholly responsive as his hands thrust her brief sweater insistently from soft curves, exploring her warm body until she seemed to be floating, her whole being burning beneath his demanding mouth. Feeling between them rose dramatically and became a kind of madness only broken, in some inexplicable fashion, by a wild sensation of pain.

A myriad of lights flashed a warning and Liza drew back through a dark haze as one of his limbs wound around hers,

'You're hurting me, please—Grant.' Her voice was a small, shaken moan, not wholly co-ordinated, against his warm mouth.

Instantly he paused, and for a brief space there was only his deep, terse breathing. Then abruptly he drew away, releasing her with a far from gentle thrust. 'I'd like to keep on,' he said curtly, his usually smooth voice metallic, 'but I'm way ahead of you, aren't I!'

'Grant . . .' Her fingers rose to bruised lips.

'Enough!' he stopped her decisively as he jumped to his feet, deliberately oppressive as he swept her swiftly up beside him. 'I'm probably more to blame than you,' his dark eyes softened slightly before the harrowed look on her taut face. 'If you were really well, Liza, if it wasn't for your damned memory, it could be another thing. As it is you wouldn't want any more complications than you have already, but don't tempt me again, there's a good girl. Not until you're really well, and perhaps mean it.'

CHAPTER SEVEN

LIZA saw very little of Grant next day. As usual he was busy in his study, and while Liza accepted this she couldn't help wondering why he had said, when he had arrived the previous morning, that he was free for the rest of the weekend. If he hadn't meant work what, then, had he referred to? she puzzled despondently as she read on the terrace until it was time for dinner.

It was quiet on the terrace and the wind on her face was cool and scented, yet she found it difficult to concentrate entirely on her book. It couldn't possibly be that Grant was still annoyed with her because she had disappointed him on the river? Well, perhaps to imagine he had been disappointed was exaggerating a little, but certainly something about her behaviour had rendered him extremely short-tempered. It hadn't taken them long to get back to Lynsend, but to Liza, aware of his continued impatience because of her naïveté, it had seemed like hours. He was not to know, nor could she possibly tell him, that she had wished passionately that they could have stayed on the boat for ever. That if he had loved her, her lack of experience would never have driven her from his arms. But such a relationship, she felt instinctively, could only be a cold thing without love, even if the clamouring of her too-responsive body had allowed her to risk it.

Before she joined the others, Liza decided to return the novel which she had managed to finish. It was one of Adrian's first successes and she hadn't told him she was reading it. He wrote science fiction, and while a lot of it was beyond her present comprehension she had enjoyed it because it belonged to a world she felt strangely familiar with. It might not be sensible that this vague feeling of being on the same frequency caused her to gravitate towards Adrian whenever she saw him. As if subconsciously she hoped he would supply the answers to much that wor-

112

ried her merely because he wrote books and she found herself intrigued by them.

It wasn't until she was putting this particular book back before choosing another that the cover of one two shelves down caught her eye. Two shades of green on cream, a monochrome presentation of fields in a foreign background. Nervously she grasped it as she drew it out.

Greece Rediscovered, and the author's name, Dean, hit Liza delicately between the eyes. How peculiar that she and this unknown writer should share the same name. A coincidence, naturally! Liza frowned, gulping a missed breath as she nervously turned the travel book over in suddenly trembling hands. Graham Dean—the name rang no clear bells, meant nothing to her. And how could it? Hadn't she worked in a shop, and weren't her parents both dead? She had no brothers or sisters, no other relatives either. Didn't Grant Latham have it on the best of authority, from those whom she had worked with and confided in all this time? No, it could only be put down to chance that her mind and hand had gone out to this particular volume almost simultaneously.

For a long moment she stood silently tense, fighting a battle with an enemy she couldn't see, then feeling suddenly ill again she thrust the book back where she had found it, as if the very feel of it scorched her. She knew a terrible desire to cry, to cling desperately to someone and weep, yet she knew she must not. Not while she remained at Lynsend. Why must Grant insist she stayed here, when every fresh torment must be endured by herself with a stiff upper lip? Such repression seemed to Liza one of the finer shades of cruelty.

After dinner, she resolved, she must seek Grant out and ask him to let her return to London. Physically and mentally, in spite of her lost memory, she could easily cope with a simple job. It would provide something to keep her mind occupied, and with girls of her own age around her she would surely recover far more quickly than she could ever hope to do down here. She would ask Grant, he must not be allowed to think her ungrateful; but no matter what his reply, Liza determined stubbornly, she would go!

Dinner that evening proved such a direct contrast to the one she and Grant had shared the night before that Liza felt more than ever like leaving. If the trip on the river had been concluded on a rather strained note it hadn't been as uncomfortable as this, with Adrian in one of his typical black moods and Paula scarcely much better. Paula spared barely a glance in Liza's direction, obviously preferring to talk to Grant and not seeming to mind that he was not particularly forthcoming. She was chatting with a forced vivacity about some friends of hers who had competed in the Atlantic Triangle but ran into trouble on the Capetown to Rio leg. Liza, feeling she had had enough of boats for the time being, let her attention stray; the conversation was not meant for her ears anyway.

Rather wistfully she gazed around the elegant table. If she couldn't honestly say she would miss overmuch the present company, she was definitely going to find it hard to do without this. The service was beautiful bone china, deeply etched and encrusted with gold, the silver lustrous, the wine glasses exquisitely hand-cut and sparkling, the lace cloth, she supposed, priceless. Was she crazy to be even contemplating turning her back on it all while she might at least have contrived to stay a few more weeks? This sort of living must grow on one, as it must certainly be vastly different from anything she had been used to.

Grant's voice, mingling with Paula's in a desultory fashion, came to Liza only from a great distance as tears rose thickly in her throat, threatening to choke her, and if his eyes quite often frowned on the fraught pallor of her face she did not notice. Grant was handsome and his house—or was it Paula's?—well-to-do, gracious, but at that moment Liza wouldn't have cared if he had lived in a bare hut on a desert island if she could have had his love, his affection.

Because throughout the meal he chose to ignore her Liza felt she must escape, and as soon as they were finished she begged to be excused. Not waiting for coffee, she ran back to her room. Adrian, she remembered, was leaving directly after dinner to fly to Paris where he had some appointment the next day. She had managed to wish him a good flight —something like that, but that was all. She should probably have said goodbye, perhaps she owed it to him, but she doubted if he would ever give such an omission a second thought. On the whole he had been nice to her, though, and if she had been staying she would have missed him, she admitted, but nothing more.

For a long while she sat by her bedroom window in the deepening twilight, looking out over the gardens, a cool green haven at this lovely soft time of night. Save for the odd call of a lone owl there was nothing to break the silence. The heavy sensuous scent of late-blooming flowers drifted up to her, tantalising her nostrils and sending a small, swift shiver down her spine. Autumn was fast approaching, she could feel it as the fitful evening breeze rustled through leaves already turning colour, drying them until they were ready to leave the slender branches to which they so tenaciously clung and drift lightly on to the water, down the river.

But before autumn really burst in all her wild glory, Liza would be gone, and she didn't think she would be altogether sorry. This might be Grant Latham's home, and while it was beautiful she had not found any real peace here. It was not a place where she would care to spend the rest of her life; nor that she would ever get the chance of doing so, she thought wryly as she rose to her feet to prepare for bed.

It was then, before she undressed, that she remembered that Grant would be returning earlier to London in the morning than was usual. Hadn't she overheard him saying something of the kind to Paula at dinner? Hastily Liza kicked off her shoes, and switching off her light swiftly left the room. Paula might already have retired and she didn't want to disturb her, nor to have to explain what she was about at this late hour. Grant, she hoped, might still be in his study, and, she prayed, in one of his more tolerant moods.

Clinging nervously to the shadow of the huge walls, Liza

went down unseen. A light still burned in the hall, but there
was no one about, and she almost stumbled with relief on
safely reaching the study door. Quickly she knocked, holding herself peculiarly rigid as if conscious of ghostly eyes,
full of disapproval, fixed on her back. It wasn't sensible to
feel wholly released from such apprehension when she
heard Grant's deep voice bidding her to come in.

Yet the few words which followed this brief order were
far from encouraging as he lifted his dark head and saw
who it was.

'Good heavens, what now? I thought it must be Paula,
although she went upstairs an hour ago.'

She was so obviously the last person he wanted to see
that Liza flinched. 'I'm sorry, Grant.' She half turned, too
ready to retreat, something that appeared to annoy him
even more than her initial intrusion.

'Come in and close the door,' he snapped, his white teeth
coming together with exasperation. 'I presume you were
unable to sleep with so much on your mind, and because
you're a woman it couldn't wait until another day!'

'How could you tell?' Her head dropped disconsolately,
his hard indifference hurting more than she liked to think.

His thick black brows shot up. 'One only needed to look
at you at dinner. You're so obviously overflowing with
whatever it is that's worrying you that I'm actually surprised you've managed to contain yourself so far. It was too
much to hope you'd decided to sleep on it, but I'd like you
to know, Liza, that I'm just one man and, as such, have my
limitations.'

Liza stood, just within the room, staring at him in a kind
of semi-trance. Yes, she could never deny it, he did work
hard. Possibly, although he seemed affluent, he didn't have
a very large staff to help him and could well do without her
and her problems!

Fervently Liza wished she had someone else to confide
in, but Paula kept an insurmountable distance and Adrian
was solely interested in himself. Now it seemed that not
even Grant wanted her. Which only, if indirectly, strength-
ened her resolve to rid him of further responsibilities.

'I'm sorry,' she said huskily, closing the door as he had ordered before approaching him across the room, her smile strained and a trifle desperate as she paused beside his desk, 'I do realise you have more than enough to do, it was actually what I wanted to talk to you about, and I wasn't sure whether you'd be back tomorrow evening or perhaps not for days.'

He looked at her a little oddly as she stood beside him. 'And so?'

'I must return to London, Grant.'

'I didn't hear that!' Something like anger touched his face, and his voice was cool and cutting.

'You did,' she assured him, a little desperately. 'I must go back!'

He drew a deep breath as if he didn't trust himself to speak, then he put out a hand and caught her fragile wrist, drawing her closer to him. 'I heard you the first time. I was simply giving you a chance to change your mind.'

'But I can't. I don't want to . . .'

'Damn it all, Liza, I have a lot to do, a lot to finish before I can hope to snatch a few hours' sleep. And now this!'

Sparks seemed to fly from where his hand grasped her arm, as the tension between them mounted. 'Do you have to swear at me all the time?' she said faintly. 'You can be terrifying.'

Something prowled in the back of his narrowed eyes. 'I've said I'm busy.'

He pulled her down with a sharply deliberate flick so that her bare elbow hit the top of his hard desk and she bit off a pained exclamation. His face was almost level, just a little above hers, and she refused to give him the satisfaction of knowing that he had hurt her. 'You don't have to spell it out,' she cried bitterly. 'I realise I'm quite the perfect nuisance, but I didn't interrupt you idly. I really do want to go home.'

'Nonsense.' Instead of accepting her brief apology, her simple statement, he sounded so horribly impatient that she could have wept. Until she remembered he hadn't always been like this—it was only since yesterday.

'Don't you see,' she gulped, 'it's the only way? I'm perfectly fit and my memory is slowly returning. Once back at the shop I should soon completely recover.'

'Liza,' Grant was suddenly very crisp, 'haven't we been through all this before? You tell me what you would do in London. Why, you wouldn't even know your way around.'

'I'd be in no worse a fix than being in—say, a strange country or city where I'd never been before. There, it's simply a matter of common sense. One soon learns, even to speak the language.'

'Go on,' he said very smoothly, as her voice trailed off uncertainly. 'You could be speaking from experience.'

'I don't know.' But her confused glance couldn't meet his cold one. 'It's just a feeling, but maybe I have been somewhere, only please don't start trying to decipher it. I've begun to recall odd things.'

'How odd?' The question came laden with sarcasm.

'I don't know.' She kept staring at his desk unhappily, completely missing his ironic tones. 'The doctor told me it often happens like this, and that my memory could come back completely at any time.'

'And here you'd be relatively safe, but in London you couldn't know what might happen!' His eyes slid over her, seeing her extreme pallor, the brilliant, dilated eyes, her slight figure in the softly clinging dress. 'You wouldn't stand a chance,' he said, so emphatically that for a moment he stilled all further protest.

Liza's soft mouth quivered with distress, and as she gazed at him despair drove her almost beyond common sense. 'If I said please, if I begged of you,' she pleaded, bending her head submissively so that the angle of it caught the light, reflecting the satiny red glow.

'You don't have to. It wouldn't work. I've understood about the wiles of women for a long time.' He was adamant as his dark eyes studied her, and there was only so much restraint. 'Look, Liza, why the sudden rush to leave? So much could depend on the next few days—weeks. Haven't we all tried to do our best? Just what's got into you?'

His voice was harsh, full of a cold suppression, as if he were driving himself forcefully in a direction other than that he would have preferred to take, but Liza only caught the discordant sound of it. He would never understand, never in a thousand years, and how could she possibly even begin to explain, after he'd been so good to her, that far from doing their best his family merely tolerated her? It was not perhaps that they meant to be deliberately unkind, but for the greater part of each day they were scarcely ever to be seen and the large house seemed to echo with loneliness. It would have been quite different if she had really belonged to the family and had had something to keep her occupied.

But all this was not easily explainable, especially to a man who appeared to have little left in the way of tolerance, and maybe Grant was right when he implied that she didn't know when she was well off.

Right now, in spite of his discouraging tones, his refusal to co-operate, she couldn't bear it when he was angry with her. 'I'm sorry, Grant.' Suddenly, before she quite realised what she was doing, she bent over and kissed him, pressing her petal-soft lips feverishly to his hard, smoothly shaven check. 'You've every right to think I'm ungrateful.'

'Aren't you?' His jaw went granite-like, as though her impulsive salute left him cold. Certainly he showed no appreciation, there was not even one flicker of response, and although she hadn't looked for any the glance he threw at her caused her cheeks to flush wildly with embarrassment. Yet how could she feel sorry—when she cared for him so much? Of course he wasn't to know that, and probably considered girls of her age too young to know their own minds. Wasn't it up to her to prove him wrong?

'If you take me back to London I'll prove just how grateful I can be,' she assured him, feeling somehow that she was being a shade reckless but unable to fight a fine desperation which carried her on.

A second ago he had been all ruthless disapproval, now he was taut with a narrowed speculation, something else again. Discerningly his hand left her wrist, travelling to her silk-clad shoulder, his eyes lingering exploringly on the sensuous curves of her lips. 'You have to convince me.' At the back of his blue eyes there flickered a small flame, but his voice was cool enough.

'Anything,' she promised, finding such blind commitment surprisingly easy, though she was unable to understand a simultaneous flare of excitement.

'I should want to see you.' He was still extremely guarded, as if fully aware of her quivering nervousness, that she was too vulnerable to her own highly-strung emotions for her own good.

'I promise...' Her voice came sweetly, sincerity trembling on every syllable. Anything to make him agree.

Grant's gaze darkened, rested thoughtfully on her luminous young profile as she momentarily glanced away. 'Are you always so eager to make rash promises?' he asked harshly.

She was back with him immediately, if rather startled by something indefinable in his face. 'Well...' she prevaricated innocently, 'wouldn't you see me every day? I mean, I'd be working for you, wouldn't I?' she pointed out reasonably.

'Liza!' He released his grasp on her shoulder but his eyes went deliberately over her, stopping exactly where the low rounded neckline of her dress exposed clearly the soft outlines of her beautiful young figure. 'Forget it,' his voice was clipped, his eyes implacable with a purposeful restraint as he stared down at her.

'Forget what?' She could feel the rapid acceleration of her heartbeats, thrown off balance as she was by every vibrant inch of him. If his meaning wasn't exactly clear why then did every taut nerve respond so violently? Physically she might be on the same wavelength, but not otherwise. There was much about him that perplexed her.

He didn't directly answer her breathless query, but his head came up swiftly, catching her wide, unwary gaze, holding it significantly until she allowed her eyes to be dominated by his, her pupils widening to liquid green-fringed pools that a man might drown in. 'Can you tell me,' he asked, softly dynamic, 'how a man should act when both his hands are tied?'

'I'm—not sure.' Was he again referring to his work? Couldn't he be more explicit? There was a strange leaping light in his eyes and his face had a hardness that unnerved her. Liza's thick lashes fluttered, falling uncertainly against heated skin. 'I don't know,' she repeated helplessly, 'but I don't want to take up any more of your time, Grant. I realise it probably wouldn't be convenient for me to leave in the morning. Apart from anything else I'm not sure that my landlady would be at home, but if you would agree to let me go within the next few days I could contact her immediately.'

He was still not entirely willing to concede to this. For a long moment he continued to stare at her, as if trying to decide what was best. She saw his mouth tighten, without realising that her too vulnerable fragility aroused a latent cruelty which must be suppressed.

Eventually he retorted slowly, 'You'd better leave it to me, Liza. If, as it seems, you're so determined to go then it might do you no harm to return to London. But give it another week. You might even be fully recovered before then. If not, a little light work might be all that's needed to jolt this elusive memory of yours. Almost I'm beginning to feel as desperate as you are.'

That hurt, though she tried not to show it. 'I've tried not to get in your way.'

Anger flicked through his face as if her wistful demeanour did not impress. 'Wouldn't you want to be a permanent feature? You have a positive flair for saying the wrong thing, Liza Dean.'

In other words he had had about enough. Being a man with such a work-motivated mind, any irrelevant problems obviously irritated. And she had been foolish enough to bestow a grateful kiss! A stranglehold of misery threatened to choke her, but this she must ignore. Tenaciously she kept her thoughts on London. 'About my job, my digs,' she began raggedly.

'The first is assured,' he replied coolly, 'and your land-lady I'll see myself.'

'No!' Why did such an idea seem strangely abhorrent? 'I can easily give her a ring, or write and tell her I'm coming if she isn't on the phone. I'd rather you didn't go there yourself.'

'What possible objection could you have? It will have to be arranged, and I'm on the spot.'

Liza hated the cold suspicion in his eyes worse than his anger. 'You might easily upset her. You have this effect on people,' she stumbled unwisely, in her search for an excuse.

'So you maintain.' Grant's voice froze several degrees colder. 'I imagine this is from personal observation, and probably I should be grateful you've noticed anything at all. I don't think you would survive if I really lost my temper with you, Liza, so for the moment we'll let that pass. Sufficient to declare that although your landlady might be one of the best, I must be personally convinced. I believe she's elderly. Your room could be damp, neglected, in need of a proper airing.'

'No . . .!' Something in her mind screamed against it.

'And I say yes!'

Was there ever such a man! 'Grant, please!'

'Liza—please!' Curtly ironic, he cut her off, his hands once more going to her shoulders, but there was no tender-ness this time in his taut fingers. 'I'm trying to be your friend, don't try me too far. You can't run your life on illogical theories you can't even explain, and you've had every concession you're likely to have from me on what we've been discussing tonight. So can't you decide to trust me and call it a day?'

'You'll forget!' Frustration was in the wide green glance she cast despairingly up at him.

'I'm a man of my word, or haven't you noticed?' With dry sarcasm he drew her towards him, bending to touch his lips to hers as he turned her to the door. 'I think I owe you that,' he suddenly grinned, 'and I shouldn't want to be in your debt.'

'When will I see you again?' While she wanted above

everything to cling, to allow the urgent inclination of her
hands to clasp his broad shoulders, Liza was aware that she
must not. But she could not restrain the anxious note in her
voice, nor did she try. It was becoming imperative that she
saw him all the time.

'I may be down through the week. If not I'll certainly
ring.'

'And a week tomorrow?'

'A week tomorrow you can, if you still want to, return
with me to London. But remember——' for a split second
he paused, as something elemental, a heightening tension,
raced between them. 'Remember,' he repeated, 'you have a
full seven days to think this over. Returning to London
could mean a greater commitment than anything you've
known so far.'

Adrian was kept in Paris longer than he had anticipated,
and, with only a rather moody Paula for company, Liza
found the ensuing days long—so long that she was almost
pleased to see him back on the Thursday. He looked tired
but not so disgruntled as she had seen him. He found her in
her usual chair in the library idly pursuing a book.

'I bumped into Grant in London,' he said sharply, without preliminaries. 'What's all this I hear about you returning to work?'

'Just that.' Liza, looking especially captivating in a soft
green sweater and slacks, glanced at him swiftly, surprised
that he appeared to be somewhat annoyed by such news.
She hadn't thought he would be interested enough to spare
even a light comment.

'How do you mean, just that?' He flung himself into the
nearest chair after pouring a liberal drink. Liza refused to
have anything.

'I think,' she said carefully, 'that it would be wiser to do
something. I can't just sit around doing nothing indefinitely.'

'Why not?' he shrugged, adding with an appreciative
grin, 'you're very decorative.'

She smiled back lightly, not bothering to protest. 'It's

nice of you to say so,' she laughed, 'but I'm probably not cut out to be an ornament.'

His grin changed slowly to a frown as he surveyed her in silence. 'If you're merely feeling restless, Liza, and it's employment you're after, why don't you help me?'

'Help you?'

'With my new book. The tentative urge I mentioned on the day we had tea in Windsor has developed into something which could be exciting, and I don't mind admitting it might have a lot to do with you. In some unobtrusive way you've grown on me, Liza. I could swear you've unlocked a door. Don't ask me why or how. I feel it's just happened.'

Liza stared at him, dismay paling her face before his absolute sincerity. 'Just coincidence,' she whispered, not wanting to have anything to do with such foolish fancies, as she believed she had already told him, if in another way.

'I don't think so,' he challenged her. 'Anyway, whether you're really responsible or not, I wouldn't mind having you around. I can't risk losing you at this stage, not with so much at stake. You don't know what it means to me, Liza,' he continued urgently, 'I haven't been able to write at all, and now this!'

Pain sharpened, moving within her. To hide it she forced a small, teasing smile. 'It's only because I'm here at this particular time. Anyone might have supplied the incentive you needed.'

He took no notice, she might never have spoken. Instead he asked abruptly, 'How would you like to do my typing? I really do need someone, I'm not offering charity.'

'But I don't type.' Liza was suddenly relieved to have such a logical excuse, seeing that Adrian did not seem prepared to take no for an answer.

'How do you know you don't?'

'I'm not sure.' He was one step ahead of her and, confused, she glanced down at her fingers. It came to her suddenly that she was able to, and so strangely did the knowledge hit her that she flinched as if physically wounded. Yet even to imagine she could type must be nonsense; hadn't she worked in a shop?

'Come here.' Adrian had a typewriter on the desk. He must have taken it from a small cupboard where the door stood open. Liza had been so nervous for a moment that she hadn't noticed. Now he stood beside the desk, slipping a piece of paper into the machine, urging her to try it, and in spite of a continuing reluctance excitement flared from some part of her, not to be resisted. It was terrible to feel so hypnotically bound by an unrelenting persuasion within her.

Mesmerised, she sat down, obeying Adrian now without protest, just an odd glance of faint desperation. Yet of their own accord, it seemed, her fingers went to the keys, finding the right ones easily, even swiftly, and it came to her unmistakably that she was quite able to cope.

'You see?' Adrian's triumphant exclamation rang in her ears as she stared numbly down at her hands, caught in amazement by her own performance. 'Didn't I tell you?' Adrian continued emphatically. 'Now you have no excuse.'

Liza straightened in her seat again but kept her eyes lowered. 'I'm sorry, I can't stay, Adrian. This—discovery, if you like—has made no difference. I realise I can type, could type. I used to type for my father. It must be a part of my memory coming back. I appear to know this, but nothing more.'

Adrian shrugged, his sudden jubilation subsiding as he turned frowning to the window, obviously ill at ease with white-faced young girls who looked as if they might pass out on him, given a hint of encouragement. 'I shouldn't worry too much about it, if I were you,' he said gruffly.

Bitterly Liza glanced at the moody set of his head. He was vastly different from Grant who, for all his ruthlessness, had never turned away when she had genuinely needed a hint of assurance. With a nervous movement of her hands she pushed away the machine in front of her; the typewriter appealed not at all. Her fingers told her she could type fairly well, but no other part of her seemed willing to co-operate. Perhaps her father, whoever he had been, had asked her to type a few letters on occasion. There was nothing to suggest she was qualified enough to take on Adrian's work. And didn't the fact that she had been work-

ing in the fashion department of a shop seem to bear this
out?

'I'm not altogether with you,' she murmured after a short
silence. 'This business of my memory is bound to worry me
a lot, but Grant, Mr Latham, I mean, has promised that I
can return to London next week. Once I'm fully occupied
again I'm sure everything will soon be all right.'

'Liza!' Adrian swung round and leaned over her, hands
on the desk. 'You're going to tell him you've changed your
mind.'

'Why should I?'

'Because I want you to. Apart from my work, for reasons
perhaps not quite clear, I must have you here.'

'No. At least, I'll think about it.' Looking up at him, she
glanced away just as quickly, not caring for the stubborn
expression on his face. Uncertainly she decided it might be
wiser not to let him think she was too adamant. She
couldn't bear to be a target for his caustic wit for the next
few days, a vulnerable victim he must wear down. 'You
must give me more time,' she said reluctantly.

'Fine.' Already his face was lightening with all the confident satisfaction of achieving his own way. He had never
considered that given a moment's reflection, Liza would
turn down his offer. Hesitation was one thing, outright rejection quite another. No girl in her right senses could pass
up a chance like this. Lynsend spelt luxurious living and,
even if neither Paula nor he owned any part of it, Grant
allowed them to use it freely. Surely if they could, a penni-
less child such as Liza Dean would not be slow to realise on
what side her bread was buttered! 'I'm sure you'll come
around to my way of thinking completely,' he added, unaware that Liza read his passing thoughts quite clearly.

Although her reluctance continued, even deepened, Liza
did help Adrian with his new book whenever he asked her.
It did provide something to do. His rough notes she typed,
then sometimes re-typed with his corrections, achieving a
turn of speed which never ceased to surprise her. But while
she delighted in the way her fingers flew nimbly over the
keys she hated the associated feeling of unease, the ex-

aggerated exhaustion from tense nerves when she retired to her room.

Many things about her former life were slowly returning. There was the size and shape of London; the district around the attic room she was trying so urgently to get back to. The shop had assumed outlines, if only hazy ones, but, while this particular knowledge cheered her, she didn't feel herself drawn to it in any way, and wondered anxiously why.

About her return to London, she grew wholly confident she was doing the right thing. It was her life before this period which mostly now continued to confuse her, and while she did her best not to brood there seemed little else she was able to do to alleviate the strain.

If only Grant had been there he might have known what to make of such curious, tormented feelings, but he was not. No use crying for the moon, she told herself bleakly. With a man there was probably no clearly drawn line to show unmistakably the hazards of bestowing even a little sympathy. Nothing to demonstrate how a little comfort given too freely could get out of hand, easily inflaming emotions already taut. There could be things, Liza reflected heavily, that she might do better to forget, not remember!

Her suspicions might be unfounded, but whatever the reason, Grant didn't come down any evening, nor did he ring. At least not to Liza personally. Paula casually mentioned that she had heard from him that morning as she paused in the hall beside Liza, on her way out.

'He did ask if you were well, my dear,' Paula smiled, 'but nothing more. Surely I didn't hear Adrian remark that you're thinking of leaving us next week?'

Liza glanced at her warily. She never knew quite where she was with Paula, and had the peculiar conviction that although Paula didn't like her she was prepared in some way to make use of her. Carefully she tried to hide the tide of hurt that swept over her because of Grant, and forced herself to answer lightly.

'You've all been very kind, but I shouldn't like to outstay my welcome.'

'Nonsense,' Paula protested, managing to sound far from sincere. 'Adrian tells me you're being an enormous help. I hope you will reconsider?'

Short, static sentences. More than ever Liza was convinced that Paula Latham would go through purgatory for her son, but wouldn't Adrian be better left to sort out his own affairs himself? But no, Paula's mind didn't work this way. Everything must be sacrificed, her own personal inclinations, those of the girl in front of her; everything, anything that might be of any help!

'I'm sorry, Mrs Latham.' Secretly dismayed by such an extravagance of maternal feelings, Liza was aware of a wild desire to escape—from what, she wasn't quite sure. Her fear might be mostly subconscious, but it was so real that it almost frightened her. Wide-eyed she stared at Adrian's mother. 'I'm sorry,' she whispered again.

'You owe it to us!' Now Paula resorted to blackmail, but Liza was forced to admit she could be right.

Liza looked at her, feeling her nerves shrivel with apprehension, aghast to hear herself say, 'I could return after a short while. Perhaps a week or two. I'm sure Mr Latham wouldn't mind . . .'

'Good heavens, girl, why should he?' Paula's voice was loaded with a sharp spite. 'So far as he goes, and I've heard plenty, women are just women—to be used as such. A girl like you could never hope to hold his attention for any length of time.'

'I wasn't aware I was hoping,' Liza gasped with emphasis, stung to anger by the woman's contemptuous tone. Yet momentarily she was glad of her own fury, hiding as it did the pain Paula's scathing words aroused. Grant—and those other women. Liza did not need, or seek, to delude herself. She was more than halfway in love with him. She also knew that as Paula said, she could never at her age hope to hold his attention very long. Perhaps she sensed that which Paula obviously didn't, that Grant was in some way attracted to the little nobody who had been rescued from his shop; but as for any permanent relationship, Liza could have told Paula that she need have no fears.

Liza felt torn. She had sensed when Grant had kissed her that he had considered it was not enough. What if he demanded an affair?

Her heart jerked. Would she have the strength to say no? He could be, when he set his mind to it she imagined, irresistible, and she herself abandoned. How was she to know? It could be that or nothing. Once his mind was made up, she suspected, he was not a man to waste time. It might stand her in good stead to have some well-guarded line of defence thought out beforehand, something which didn't show.

Liza stood, her hand hard over her racing heart, scarcely hearing Paula's voice cut through her tumultuous thoughts, just vaguely aware that Paula's manner changed, becoming almost reconciliatory.

'I really don't know why we're allowing Grant to upset us, Liza. After all, we're really discussing Adrian. He's the one who matters, as I expect you'll agree.'

Without answering Liza gazed at her mutely, unable even to return Paula's light smile. All she had an urge to do was flee.

CHAPTER EIGHT

LIZA became anxious when Grant didn't return until the Sunday evening, and it didn't help that when he did arrive, he seemed to be in rather a strange mood. He spoke to her only briefly, barely glancing in her direction at all as she lingered in the hall, and she stared after him with a sinking heart as she watched him go upstairs to change for dinner.

She was simply being silly, fanciful, she tried to reassure herself as Adrian passed her a sherry. Yet she was still unable to dismiss the unhappy suspicion that, for some reason or another, he had momentarily found it almost impossible to look at her.

Dinner did not appear to bring much improvement. Grant seemed preoccupied, not talking a great deal, and the atmosphere could only be described as slightly strained. Only once did Liza catch Grant's dark blue eyes on her, and then he was not smiling but looking at her as if she was almost his enemy. She looked away from the cruel little twist near his mouth, the colour leaving her face although she was not aware of it. The hardness in his eyes did not escape her; yet what, she wondered half desperately, had she ever done to deserve it?

After dinner she made an inaudible excuse and escaped to the library, where despondently she switched on the television set which stood there. Shortly afterwards, to her surprise, Grant followed her.

'Why didn't you stay and have coffee with us?' he asked curtly, placing a full cup by her side. 'Haven't you ever been taught that as a house guest, you do owe your hostess at least a modicum of courtesy? It wouldn't have hurt you to pretend a certain politeness.'

'Even should I not feel it, you mean?' Defiance, mingled with pain, almost choked her. 'I can assure you that my refusal to stay for coffee had nothing directly to do with Mrs Latham. I was simply being tactful. You've only been here an hour. I was merely giving you an opportunity to discuss things that were not perhaps for—a house guest's ears.'

If she had expected her apparent tactfulness to be appreciated she was doomed to disappointment. Grant merely glanced at her coolly, dismissing the subject as though it had never arisen. 'Drink your coffee while it's still hot,' was all he said.

Liza regretted she could not resist saying, 'I've been looking for you all weekend...' She didn't intend it to sound like a query, but she knew it came out like one.

No one ever questioned Grant Latham's movements, she could see it right away, and an odd little shiver ran fearfully down her spine as his eyes went black. 'I had other things to do,' he supplied tersely, 'mostly concerning you.'

'Me?' Liza's mind went blank.

His eyes, grim with hidden speculation, ran over her. 'I've been arranging that your room should be ready. You can take tomorrow to settle in. I've also had a long talk with Miss Russell, the head of your particular department; she'll look after you personally.'

'Oh, thank you, Grant!' Liza's voice was suddenly warm with gratitude. She ought to have trusted him. She felt quite ashamed of her sulks! He worked hard and no doubt was tired. The dark grey lounge suit he wore appeared to accentuate the grim lines on his face, the unrelenting angle of his jaw. He looked so tall, strongly built, with a dark force of leashed energy running powerfully through him, but in that moment Liza felt too full of pleasure to be frightened. Swiftly impulsive, she scrambled to her feet and ran to his side, her face warm with betraying emotions as she clasped his arm.

Eagerly she gazed up at him, the glowing dark red of her

hair spilling across her shoulders, her eyes a startling clear green through a thick density of lashes. 'I really had so much to tell you,' she hesitated charmingly, appealingly. 'You might not consider it important, but to me it is. I've been so absolutely bursting with news, and I did miss you.'

For one taut instant she felt him stiffen before he slowly relaxed, in everything except his narrowed eyes. He still remained watchful—hostile. Bewildered, Liza searched for the right word, even while she told herself again that she imagined it, that he was only tired.

'Won't you sit down, Grant? Can't I get you a drink?' So eager was she of a sudden to please him that she refused to admit his air of cold contemplation, or the almost visible anger which stirred within him as he stared down at the lovely face upraised to his.

'No, thank you,' he replied at last. 'And you'd better tell me your news, as I may have to go out again shortly.'

'I see.' Liza's voice sank unhappily, swiftly deflated, her renewed hopes of a cosy hour or two fading. She frowned slightly and her green eyes dropped to the restrained pattern on his smart tie. He was different this evening, but why or how, she could not be sure. 'It doesn't really matter, about my news, I mean,' she said with a heaviness of heart.

'What is it?'

Why did he have to sound so impatient, like a man at the end of his tether? Yet still there was an urge within her to humour him, to show forbearance. 'I've been helping Adrian with his new book,' she began, not presenting things as wisely as she might have done.

'Really.' Grant Latham's voice was clipped as he moved abruptly away from her.

'Yes. He would like me to stay, but I refused, although I do feel I owe him something. You see, while I was busy I remembered I'd typed for my father.'

'You remembered that!'

Now he was actually interested. Indeed his glance was very alert. Not that Liza noticed with her bright head bent. She nodded, adding wistfully, 'But there was nothing more.

Not where or why, if you know what I mean? However, it's a start.'

'Of course.'

Did he have to stare at her as if he were not quite sure what to make of it, of her? 'And,' she faltered, 'I've remembered quite a lot about London.'

'Such as?'

Swallowing quickly in the face of such obviously forced interest, Liza continued, 'Well, broadly speaking, I suppose. The size of it and so on.'

'Where you lived?'

'No, not exactly. Just something of the district. At least I think it must be that particular district.'

At once he appeared to relax, even as far as smiling at her for what she thought was the first time since he had arrived home. 'This can only be useful,' he assured her. 'I'll feel happier that you can find your way around.'

'I can't remember the shop,' she apologised ruefully, less tense now that his mood appeared to be lighter. 'I can recall such places as Buckingham Palace, the Houses of Parliament. Big things . . .'

'Big things,' his smile quirked a little as he came back to her, startling her by grasping her waist with long lean fingers, a determination that took her breath away. 'We'll leave in the morning,' he said softly, his eyes holding hers relentlessly as one of his hands slid slowly upwards, deliberately exploring pronounced curves until, just as Liza's legs threatened to crumple under her, it came to rest against her tender nape. 'Don't let Adrian influence you and persuade you to stay against your will. He wants a prop, not a secretary.'

He held her in a vice while, gasping, she tried to leave him. 'I'm glad—I mean about going.' Her mind was in a kind of painful turmoil. She hadn't one thought in her head to spare for Adrian. Her whole body seemed on fire, but also completely without the ability to move. 'Thank you again for taking me,' she whispered through shaking lips.

'Which will do to begin with,' he exclaimed enigmatically, catching the point of her chin and dropping a hard kiss on her mouth before he released her, left her. 'Make sure you're ready,' he added as he went through the door.

Next day in London, Liza thought she must have dreamt the whole episode. All through the night, conscious of her increasing vulnerability, she had determined she would never go to London with Grant Latham! That she would simply work a few weeks for Adrian, then find another job elsewhere. Yet here she was travelling by Grant's side, completely unable to withstand him. Perhaps, she tried to excuse herself, it was because she still hoped she could be useful to him?

Keenly as Liza had imagined she had looked forward to returning, once in London she found herself contrarily missing the quietness of the countryside. The traffic roared, the noise seeming to drum in her ears, and she shivered, closing her eyes as if wishing to block out both sight and sound.

'You were determined.' There was a cynical impatience in Grant's face, although the glance he threw at her held also the faintest hint of concern.

'To come—yes, I was,' she agreed without opening her eyes, not willing right then to meet his coolly appraising ones. He was too astute, he could read thoughts she imagined well concealed. And while she might have been too precipitate in her decision to return, she wouldn't alter it. It was something she felt deep down inside her, that she had to do whatever the consequences, and behind closed eyelids lay a modicum of protection.

'Look at me. Your surroundings. You're back home, if you like to call it that!'

This time there was no disputing the command in his deep voice. Up she sat, her heart pounding as her eyes opened wide. Grant had parked in front of a block of modern flats. Or it was a building of some sort, with the green area around obviously private, very expensive! Even the beautifully placed trees looked out of the top drawer with their elegantly arranged foliage of glossy greens and gold. The sweeping fir on their right looked positively regal.

'I don't seem to remember any of this,' exclaimed Liza, a tiny frown of uncertainty creasing her brow. She sat up straighter, a flutter of unexplainable uneasiness catching at her throat as the smartness of the area impressed itself further upon her. 'This surely can't be where I lived? It doesn't seem the kind of place I could possibly afford.'

'Take it easy.' Grant's firm hand on her arm came as a calming influence. 'For a girl who can't remember it's remarkable what you come up with.' His voice was extremely dry, but Liza still stirred anxiously and didn't notice. 'As a matter of fact,' he added coolly, 'this need only be temporary. Your old landlady hasn't been too well and has gone to her sisters for a few weeks. She told me quite frankly that she intended to shut up her house while she was away, and this was all I could find at practically a moment's notice.'

'Possibly.' This much Liza would concede. 'But there's nothing to stop me trying, is there?' Her new panic, a feeling of being trapped and the associated alarm she felt, showed clearly in the wide-eyed gaze she turned on him.

'You could,' he agreed suavely, his mouth tightening, 'but I only got this because I happened to know someone with the right connections. You just try, Liza. Go right ahead.'

'I will.' She had to defy him all the way, otherwise she would never survive!

'And I suppose you can afford the appropriate hotel charges while you're looking?'

'Hotel charges?' She was staring at him now with more than a hint of desperation. 'Money!' she whispered, as if it had almost just occurred to her. It wasn't conceivable that she hadn't even thought about it until this moment. She had found a couple of pounds in her handbag at Lynsend, but she had forgotten completely about it. At Lynsend she had never needed any. She had found everything in her room she could possibly require, but she must have been singularly stupid not to have foreseen this! It was going to be terrible if she must perforce borrow from Grant Latham

until she began earning. Of course she was going to begin
working right away...

But his voice cut smoothly through her thoughts, ruthlessly dissipating her momentary confidence. 'Most private
people with any kind of accommodation to let demand at
least a week's rent in advance. To protect themselves,
naturally. I suppose you know that?'

'No.'

'Well, you do now, so I suggest you stop arguing and
allow me to show you your new home. Otherwise the porter
might imagine we mean to sit here all day.'

Was there nothing she could do but obey? To follow him
unhappily on feet which stumbled, caught between him and
the man behind who carried her bags. Liza was scarcely
aware of anything at all until they arrived at the door of
what appeared to be a very luxurious apartment.

The porter dismissed, she stared around. At the medium-
sized lounge with two doors leading off it. One into the
bedroom, Grant told her, the other to a small but well
equipped kitchenette. The bedroom door stood open and
Grant walked straight through with the heaviest of her luggage. The carpet, Liza noticed, was white, the pile looking
almost deeper than that which she stood on.

'Like it?' Grant queried, and she was suddenly aware
that he was again by her side, watching her closely.

'Who wouldn't?' Nervously trying to take everything in
at once, Liza missed his faint air of derisive satisfaction.
Some inner emotion was working on her, paling her face
until every feature, even the vulnerable curves of her sensuous mouth were clearly if unconsciously defined. 'It's
quite wonderful, Grant, and thank you. Of course I must
pay the rent myself. I will also repay anything else I owe
you from my first wages.'

'Naturally.'

She was relieved that he did not argue even if his voice
was taut. Anxiously, as he silently watched her, she bit her
lip, unable to refrain from asking, 'Will it be an awful
lot—my rent, I mean? You'll have to tell me how much
and whom I should pay it to. You see, I have no idea.'

His eyes glinted as they moved over her face, lingering consideringly on the deep cleft above her upper lip. 'Stop worrying,' he growled, 'everything has been arranged. The girl in the office will see to it, she has everything in hand.' He named an extremely low figure, and relieved, Liza nodded. She could just about manage that. Her salary from the shop would surely cover such a modest sum. It might even be possible to stay here permanently if this was all they asked.

Feeling more independent than she had done for some time, she smiled gratefully up at him, only to find herself being pushed firmly towards the kitchenette. 'You'd better convince me,' he smiled, 'before I go, that you're capable of making a cup of tea. I could certainly do with one.'

'But of course, Mr Latham,' she smiled back, more relaxed with him than she had been all day.

They hadn't left Lynsend until after lunch and Liza was thirsty rather than hungry. Grant too declined anything to eat as he followed her, watching moodily while she filled the kettle and plugged it in. The smart new kitchen with its gleaming appointments reflected their images so closely together, so clearly outlined in the small space that Liza flinched, stubbornly averting her eyes from the mirror-like surfaces.

'You'll do,' he said later as they sat in the lounge, drinking the fragrant tea. Swiftly he drained his cup, noting how Liza's eyes were shadowed with weariness. 'Rest now,' he ordered briefly, getting to his feet, 'I'll call for you later and take you out to dinner. You can't spend the evening cooped up here on your own, however nice you consider it to be.'

After he had gone, Liza stared despairingly at the closed door. She wasn't really eager to have dinner with him, yet how could she have refused? A headache or another excuse would cut no ice with a man like him. Perhaps it wasn't logical to feel that in some way he imagined he owned her and was slowly but deviously consolidating his claim. She loved him, or thought she loved him, but how was she to know? Might not she have cared for someone else, a man who might still be waiting—somewhere? In spite of her suspicions it was probably merely an outsize conscience that drove Grant to be so kind, but she herself had no such simple motive. Grant drew from her a response which she was sure she could not have felt for anyone else, but from the blank obscurity of the past how could she be certain?

Maybe she would have been wiser to have stayed at Lynsend and helped Adrian. He hadn't taken it very well when she had insisted that morning that she was definitely leaving, and Paula had been frankly annoyed. If it hadn't been for Grant she doubted if she would have had the strength to stand out against their combined disapproval. Oh, well, Liza shrugged helplessly, it might not have worked, anyway. Adrian was becoming too possessive. He'd been quite bitter when Grant had told him that he was taking Liza back to London immediately after lunch, his sharpness managing to make Liza feel both guilty and uncomfortable.

Trying to push such depressing thoughts to one side, she began to explore the flat more methodically than she had done so far, finishing up in the bathroom which adjoined the exceedingly smart bedroom. As in the kitchen, the gleaming fitments continued to intrigue her and the sunken aquamarine bath she found enchanting. The colour actually suited her, too, she decided with surprise, surveying herself in the mirrored wall as, with her silken hair piled on top of her head, she relaxed in the deep scented water. Grimacing wryly, she tried to laugh at her too sober reflection. She should, she decided, be one of the happiest girls in the world, not the most dejected!

Snap out of it, she advised herself morosely when, minutes later, clad only in a silken wrap, she flung herself across the bed. Rest, Grant had instructed, before dinner. From habit she tried to obey him. The flat was warm and eventually, encouraged by the superb softness of a well sprung mattress, she fell asleep, and it was almost eight before she woke to find the doorbell ringing.

Momentarily startled, without being completely conscious of what she was doing, she rolled hastily off the bed and rushed to answer it. Grant had returned. Tall and distinguished in a dark dinner jacket, he stood on the doorstep, and though instinctively Liza had known who it would be she blinked as she gazed up at him, still half asleep.

His eyes ran swiftly but not approvingly over her. 'Does it come naturally to you to answer the door like this?' he asked sharply, staring at her, his face grim with an emotion Liza's confused mind could only describe as dislike.

A wild flush rose to her cheeks and she pushed at the loose coils of her hair, thrusting them distractedly behind her ears in an overwrought fashion. Did he have to stand there looking at her like that? 'I'm sorry, Grant,' at last she found her voice, even if it quavered, 'I'm afraid I dozed off ...'

'Really?'

Her flush deepening painfully at his tone, Liza backed away from him defensively, into the room. 'You did tell me to rest,' she choked, 'and when I heard the doorbell I must have got a fright. I didn't stop to think.'

'Obviously not. Do you ever, I wonder?' The cutting edge to his voice was still in evidence. 'Have you also forgotten we're going out?'

'No. At least—no, I hadn't,' she stammered. 'If you'll just give me ten minutes?'

Some faint perfume hung between them, the fragrant bath essence which clung to her skin and hair, transmuted into something very tantalising through the clinging thinness of her robe. She became aware he was studying her in a very curious fashion. A light flashed in his eyes and his mouth curved grimly, expressing immediately the hard maleness of him. Suddenly, his glance perfectly hard and steady, he reached for her, pulling her fragile lightness to him, into his arms.

'Would you rather not go out?' he inquired, his lips against her ear, devastatingly provocative. 'It could be extremely pleasant to stay here.'

'No, it wouldn't!' Liza's reaction was instinctive, and again the colour swept up under her skin, lending lustre to the rather frantic expression in her green eyes. Grant held her firmly against him, almost hurting her against the hardness of his arms, yet it seemed he could be taunting her emotions rather than his own. His were so controlled and disciplined as to make him wholly invulnerable, but hers were another thing!

His mouth was touching hers now, sliding to her neck, while one of his hands had grasped her bare arm, his fingers smoothing the warm skin as though it were silk. Back came his lips to hers again, forcing them sensuously apart, a lesson in loving that sent the blood spinning to Liza's head, her pulses hammering primitively. His passion was covered only by the thinnest veneer and flickers of abandoned excitement and fright rushed through her, allowing her to believe she had never known anything like it. It was as if there was a smouldering fire burning between them, ready and willing to consume them both with flames.

For a few seconds Liza felt her traitorous body respond impulsively before panic won at least a temporary victory and she wrenched herself away from him. 'I feel like going out,' she heard herself crying wildly, almost visibly having to fight an overwhelming desire to fling herself into his arms again. Why did he have to just stand there, alert, yet motionless? A relentless predator, simply biding his time! Wherever—catching her breath, Liza pressed shaking hands to her hot forehead—had that idea come from?

'As you wish.' The bored indifference hurt when, as suddenly as he had taken her, he let her go, not intending to tolerate anything so juvenile as a struggle. When he chose, his expression plainly stated, she would not so easily escape him. 'Go and dress,' he agreed, thrusting her quickly from him, a man with victory almost within his grasp, but who believed in finesse rather than hurry.

Hours later, in the taxi returning home, Liza found herself again wondering why Grant did it. Why he should choose at moments to treat her as if she were an experienced woman, one who he was convinced looked for something more than a few light kisses? This, combined with a kind of slow-burning anger in him when he held her, she seemed to sense instinctively. Did he, she wondered, know something about her she didn't know herself? There seemed no end to the number of confusing questions to which she could find no answer. She only knew she must do something very soon, otherwise how could she continue to resist him?

Now he lounged beside her, but well away, keeping his distance, almost giving the impression he was a stranger. That he had never so much as had her in his arms, let alone kissed her. He had been friendly, perfectly courteous but somewhat unapproachable all evening. All the time, apart from when they had danced.

They had dined in the West End at a smaller place Grant knew. At least he had assured her it was one of the smaller, less popular night spots, but to Liza it had looked very expensive and exclusive. They had eaten a delicious meal and danced a little. Liza had stared at him doubtfully when he had suggested it, and had been somewhat incredulous to find that she could manage. Almost as if she had no will of her own she had found herself responding completely to Grant's every movement, her steps, her whole being following his expert guidance trustfully, and had known a feeling of oneness she could never have denied.

If the soft lights, the curiously intimate atmosphere had been a trap specially set for the unwary to ensnare the senses, Liza had not had the slightest inclination in her head to avoid it. Grant had held her in his arms and moved with such practised ease that she had found herself floating. For a moment his cheek had been against her hair and it had seemed the most natural thing in the world to be dancing with him.

Afterwards Grant had taken her to his mews home in Kensington, and she had been alarmed afresh by its luxurious comfort. Not that this had been something he had allowed her to dwell on. He had insisted she helped him make coffee, which he had carried into the lounge, explaining on the way that he only employed a daily woman, not a housekeeper.

Liza thought she had understood. 'I suppose such a person would be expensive,' she had said, enjoying the excellent coffee but refusing the brandy he poured with it.

'You could say that,' he had drawled, glancing at her quickly, 'but it also,' he had seemed to add deliberately, 'gives me more freedom, not to have someone else actually living here.'

What exactly had he meant by that? Liza pondered his words idly, leaning back in her corner of the taxi, unaware of how her red hair gleamed lustrously against the dark leather. There was so much about this man she did not know or understand. This evening she had tried hard to please him by wearing one of her smartest gowns, and she knew she looked her best. Not that this was so very difficult in a dress which must have cost a great deal of money, but she had known right away, from the expression on his face, that he had considered her well worth waiting for.

Her smooth brow pleated suddenly as she glanced unhappily down at the soft fullness of her pale skirt, her unconsciously deep sigh bringing his head around sharply.

'What is it?' he asked, with an alertness not usual at that early hour of the morning.

'My clothes,' she faltered. 'I mean,' she stumbled as his dark eyebrows rose, 'I can scarcely continue wearing these you've lent me. I was thinking that my own clothes must still be in my old room, but if my landlady is away how can I get them?'

'Don't be so stupid.' He relaxed. 'What possible use would the dress you're wearing now be to anyone else? Any of your clothes for that matter. You may as well keep them. Wear them until they're threadbare, if you like.'

She giggled then, spontaneously, almost flirtatiously, had she but known it. 'You're going to need an extremely thrifty wife, Mr Latham!'

Immediately she could have bitten her tongue out. Almost she did, beneath his oddly speculative stare.

'Wouldn't you care to be a possible candidate?' he asked smoothly.

'I'm sorry—I mean, of course not.' She was suddenly breathless, and conscious that he knew it.

His eyes entangled with her own, mocking her. 'Such

emphatic denial is scarcely flattering, my dear. I'm not sure that thrifty would be correctly descriptive of the woman I should choose to have for a wife. I do know she'd have to be very generous.'

Again, Liza decided angrily, the double meaning! Why did he have to twist everything she said to suit his own ends? Quickly she dragged her wide-eyed gaze from his enigmatic face to stare through the window, watching how the street lighting reflected weirdly in the wet pavements the never-ending acres of shining, plate-glass windows. Water streamed and a cool little wind blew warningly. Summer was over, Liza thought dismally, not certain that it had ever been.

She was almost relieved when on reaching the flat, Grant left again almost immediately, after promising to pick her up some time after ten later that morning.

'Your first day,' he replied quite firmly, when she protested she would rather go earlier. 'You'll find ten is quite early enough.'

To Liza's surprise, after what she could only describe as an unsettling evening, she slept soundly, but after she woke, during the hours which followed she was to receive something of a shock, and to find that they rarely come singly!

At half-past eight she got up and, after a quick shower, dressed, before going to make herself a cup of tea. Because Grant had arrived in such a hurry the previous night and provided her with dinner, she had forgotten all about provisions. She hadn't even thought of looking for any in the array of fitted units, but she did remember that she had intended asking him where she could shop. Now, to her amazement, she found enough food to keep her for weeks in the huge fridge-freezer in the kitchen. In the cupboards, too, there seemed a wide variety of everything she could possibly need. There was positively everything from frozen meat down to bacon and cereals and fruit juices. Even bread and milk, butter, salt and pepper; there wasn't a thing missing she could think of!

It must have cost a small fortune! Gulping rapidly, her

face white with returning anxiety, Liza groped numbly for
a slice of bread to pop into the elegant toaster. How could
she ever repay it all? It would take weeks, months, so long
that she didn't care to think about it! One thing, she determined there and then, it had to stop. It wasn't as if she had
ever asked for anything. If Grant enjoyed playing godfather
then he must simply find someone else. She would speak to
him as soon as he arrived. There would not be a better
opportunity.

But that morning there was no opportunity, none whatsoever. Grant had promised he would pick her up, but instead he sent a car for her.

'Mr Latham couldn't make it, miss,' a man announced
brightly when she answered the door. He touched his
peaked cap respectfully, but his eyes were full of uncon-
cealed curiosity as he stared her up and down. 'I'm to take
you in to work, miss, seeing it's your first day. I hear you're
the young lady who was injured in the fire.'

'Yes. Good morning, but I'm all right now,' Liza assured
him hastily,-with not a little confusion, having had an entirely different kind of speech carefully prepared. She was
surprised to find, too, that in spite of her annoyance about
the food, because Grant had not come, she missed him and
was unreasonably disappointed, when she opened the door,
not to find him standing on her doorstep.

'If you would just wait a minute while I get my coat,' she
murmured, turning to dive back inside. She had been going
to ask Grant in for coffee, as it was just about that time.

'I expect Mr Latham is busy,' she said lightly as they
sped swiftly across the city. Now that she was actually on
her way she found herself beset by a nervousness such as
she had not anticipated. It was a frightening terror, prowling within her, forcing her to seek distraction in conversation she might otherwise have avoided. 'Should you
not have been helping him?' she added. 'I could easily have
found my way here by tube.'

The man laughed. 'I don't happen to be that far up the
ladder, dear. I don't personally imagine I'd be much help to
the likes of him! And as for being busy—well, I expect he

was, in a way. The last time I saw him he was following Miss Davina Courtland into her old man's Rolls! But I guess some people would call that hard work.'

Liza didn't hear the driver's dry tones. She was only aware of the sudden pain in her heart, and that it deepened as the man observed more soberly, 'We think, the staff that is, that there could be a wedding soon.'

'I find it more convenient not to have a housekeeper.' Grant's words spun back to Liza tauntingly. Was this what he had meant? Yet what business was it of Liza Dean's, a girl whom he had merely befriended?

Rather desperately she tried to think of something else, but her mind refused to be diverted. The thought of Grant entertaining another girl in his delightful mews home, making love to her, perhaps, was scarcely bearable, and unhappily Liza realised that she was probably suffering from the first tortuous pangs of jealousy. The news that Grant Latham was seriously involved with a Miss Courtland should, Liza told herself firmly, make her feel better about the flat. To know that Grant must have acted on a purely impersonal basis was at least comforting. Or should have been if she hadn't felt too muddled to see anything clearly!

'You're certainly a good-looker, miss, if you don't mind me saying so.' The driver, no doubt wondering at her sudden silence, was peering at her curiously through his mirror, 'It's a good job the fire did no lasting damage.'

'Thank you.' Liza tried to smile because she sensed that such a remark should be appreciated, but while he seemed quite a nice little man, she wished he wouldn't keep furtively peering at her.

She stared fixedly at the back of his capped head, avoiding his assessing gaze and trying to look supremely indifferent. It wasn't easy not to think exclusively of Grant, a state of affairs which was becoming, she admitted, too much of a habit. 'Have we met before?' she asked the man at last.

'I wish we had, love!' he laughed wryly, 'but no, we haven't. In any case you'd never remember me among the hundreds of staff.'

Hundreds of staff? Liza's nerves jerked with a new, barely recognisable apprehension as the car left the central road and seemed literally to dive underground. She had been so busy concentrating on other things that she had scarcely once looked to see where they were going. They might well have been travelling over a deserted moor, instead of one of the world's largest cities. 'Where are we?' she gasped breathlessly.

'Underground car park. The firm's,' the man grunted. 'I'll take you straight up. I believe your boss is waiting.'

Boss? Surely he didn't mean Grant? 'You said boss?' she asked as she climbed from the car.

'Your fashion supervisor, Miss Russell. I don't always remember their names, but Miss Russell, the old dear, has been here almost as long as I have.'

'Oh, I see.' Liza frowned as she hurried after him, pretending to understand something she didn't. The garage was large, too dimly lit to see into its far-reaching corners, but it hadn't the appearance of belonging to any small establishment. There were numerous cars parked around, and trucks and huge trailers with *Lathams* slashed in large lettering across their sides. Men who looked as if they might be mechanics or drivers hurried to and fro, none of them taking the slightest notice of Liza, although she did see one nod carelessly to her companion. She was surprised to find her legs functioning normally, but otherwise she felt dazed.

'Up you go.' Her escort hustled her into a lift, and pressed a button which shot the bare steel monster upwards.

'Couldn't I go the rest of the way myself?' Liza suggested, discovering her wits at last.

'Not a hope, darlin',' he replied with a cheery grin. 'It's as much as my life's worth to lose sight of you.' As if to demonstrate he slicked a lightning finger across his wrinkled brown throat. 'Old as I am, I have no wish to die yet!'

The luminous dial told Liza clearly that there were numerous floors, but as it was a staff lift it didn't stop and no one else got in. 'How many departments are there?' she asked, feeling more than slightly puzzled.

'Dozens, dearie,' the man obliged absently as they drew nearer the fashion floor, 'but then you've got to expect it when Lathams is one of the largest stores in London. Or didn't you know?'

'No,' Liza whispered, receiving her third shock of the morning as the lift stopped and she walked numbly out.

CHAPTER NINE

MISS RUSSELL saw Liza almost at once and welcomed her with almost open arms.

'My dear,' she gushed, rushing forward effusively, 'how good it is to have you back again!' Disregarding the slightly raised eyebrows of one or two nearby assistants, she clasped Liza's hands warmly.

The sceptical eyebrows didn't alarm Liza at all as she just didn't see them. She was much too busy concentrating on Miss Russell, whom to her delight she seemed to recall, if only vaguely. And even if it was only Miss Russell's face that seemed familiar, it did seem to make a promising start. There was nothing to warn her that Miss Russell, in greeting her so enthusiastically, was acting very much out of character.

Liza simply smiled trustingly in return and murmured that she was happy to be back.

At that time of the morning the department was not really busy and Liza soon found herself at the centre of a small group of young women who wavered curiously between surprise and concern when she failed to recognise them. There was only one, named Chloe, towards whom Liza found her eyes returning constantly.

After a few minutes, however, noticing Liza's increasing bewilderment, Miss Russell chased them away, with the exception of Chloe.

'Chloe will show you what to do, dear,' she smiled, 'and it will probably be wiser to stay near her until your memory returns completely. It will all seem strange at first, but you and Chloe were good friends and she'll look after you. Mr

Grant has arranged for our staff nurse to look in later, just in case you find your first day too much of a strain. Of course he tells me you will also be continuing your outside treatment and will have time off for this.'

Miss Russell sounded so much like a fond, fussing parent that Liza, to her dismay, found tears not far away. Wistfully her thoughts flew to Grant's stepmother. Mrs Latham had little of this other woman's kindness.

In this, Liza discovered, she might be slightly mistaken.

'Dear me!' Chloe exclaimed hoarsely, before they had gone many yards, 'I've never known old Russell so—what's the word?—magnanimous. What have you done to deserve it, Dean? Or perhaps, more to the point, how have you managed to achieve it?'

'Isn't she always like that? Kind, I mean.'

'Ha! I can see you don't remember!'

Liza stared at her doubtfully. This girl seemed fond of low whispers. Maybe, too, of a little exaggeration. But it was obvious that Chloe meant well and that they had known each other in the past. If, as Miss Russell maintained they had been good friends, then there could be no good reason not to trust her. It might simply be better not to take what she said too seriously, or better still, to ignore much of it completely.

'There's bound to be a lot of things it would be more convenient to know,' Liza replied evasively, attempting to divert Chloe from Miss Russell. Yet, unwittingly, these few words only seemed to recall other, more alarming confusions. Impulsively she halted, turning anxiously around. 'The man who brought me here this morning—he told me Lathams is one of the largest stores in London.'

'Yes,' Cloe nodded absently as she watched a possible customer moving towards them. 'Joe, that would be.'

'But was he right about Lathams?' Liza's face was white and Chloe glanced at her quickly.

'Well, yes,' she frowned uncertainly, aware suddenly that Liza was upset, if not sure why. 'There are a lot of large stores in London, of course.'

'I suppose so, yes.' Liza's bright head fell. 'I expect it's just one more thing I forgot.'

'The size, you mean?'

Chloe sounded too sharply curious. Liza nodded, unhappily. 'I was foolish enough to believe it would be as I imagined it,' she admitted.

'You'll soon get used to it again.'

'Yes.' Once more, for no clear reason, Liza felt tears threatening and said quickly, 'Gr— I mean, Mr Latham has been very kind, but it might have been kinder to have explained about this.'

Chloe frowned, not wholly following. 'He probably never gave it a thought. He leads a very busy life.'

They don't understand, Liza reflected desperately.

The girl Chloe watched hesitated and moved on. Chloe shrugged, giving Liza her whole attention. 'He didn't want you worried in any way—this I do know. That was why he refused to let us visit you in hospital, for fear we inadvertently alarmed you. Which, he said, would do more harm than good. It probably wouldn't have made much difference as in any case you wouldn't have known me, but I must say I felt a bit of a traitor, seeing that we were friends and all that.'

Chloe did sound a little regretful, but she also seemed slightly reproachful, as if she privately considered that Liza was dwelling too much on what was past. Liza gazed after her as she went to attend a customer who this time was not merely 'just looking'.

Liza knew she ought to have followed but for the moment didn't seem able to move. None of this, in spite of Chloe's reassurance, made sense! Liza's apprehensive gaze wandered the length of the extremely modern department, noting the professional, artistic touches, the attractiveness of the general decor, the skilled arrangement of clothes. To one side of the department she noticed a gilded alcove with *Couturier Clothes* sketched discreetly above it, with elegantly painted doors leading off. Miss Russell, she saw, was ushering two beautifully dressed women through one of them, women who looked expensive from the feet up.

'None of your ready-mades there!' Chloe was back, whispering again. 'All models in that exclusive annexe, some costing more than I make in months. Even the air in there is pricey!'

Liza tried to smile, but the more she learned throughout the day, the more resentful she grew, until she felt she could never bear to look at Grant Latham again. It didn't seem possible, after learning how much he owned, to imagine they could ever have been friends, and the longer she thought about it the more suspicious she became. Not that the general atmosphere in the department helped very much, with everyone from Miss Russell downwards treating her like a VIP, something which Liza found more alarming than flattering. When, after lunch, she plucked up sufficient courage to assure Miss Russell there was no need for any special treatment, all she received was a rather evasive reply.

'Wouldn't you have had patience with me, my dear, if I'd been in your shoes? But for you, Liza, the store, or at least this part of it, might have been burnt down, and many of us could have been seeking new jobs. So you must allow us to be nice to you, dear. If nothing else it's good for us to show a proper appreciation.'

Liza despaired, feeling almost too disheartened to protest when, at four o'clock, her cheerful driver of the morning appeared.

'Home for you now, dear.' Miss Russell's smile was determined, and while perfectly friendly clearly indicated that she would brook no refusal. 'Mr Latham's orders precisely! You are not to overdo things, especially on your first day. You've done very well as it is. Now you must go home and rest.'

'Yes,' Liza agreed automatically, already realising the futility of argument with Miss Russell. Numbly she went to seek her coat. She had seen nothing of Grant all day.

It hadn't seemed worth making an issue of it, she shrugged, as she let herself into the flat a little later. Everyone had been so emphatic that she didn't overwork that she had found herself left with practically nothing to do, and now she didn't feel particularly tired. Tense rather than tired, she supposed, but decided that her exhaustion was not physical, but composed of so many other things which she couldn't—or wouldn't—begin to dissect. If she had done so, and at the same time been perfectly honest with herself, she could have admitted that most of her inner turmoil was directly related to not having seen Grant. At that moment, however, Liza was far from being ready to be honest with herself or—anyone else.

Scarcely aware of what she was doing, she hung away her outdoor clothes and changed into another dress, a soft, light silk, as the flat was warm. Moodily she removed the pins from her coiled hair and brushed it out until it hung thick and fluffy across her shoulders, the movement of the brush slowly releasing the tight band of tension from around her forehead, if not from her heart.

She still felt full of distracted tremblings, and readily blamed Grant. Too much had been bottled up all day, and the state of her temper was something he must have known about, but he hadn't come near her. Realising what she would have had to say about everything, including the size of the—shop, he had obviously made a point of keeping out of her way!

Once she had been tempted to ask the way to his office, but had desisted, pride stopping her just in time. What she had to say must be said in private, not with other people around. Most probably, though, he might not have been in his office, and although she did not admit it, she had shrunk from discovering that he was still out with this girl called Davina Courtland. That, she hadn't felt able to risk. She hadn't wanted to know!

Grant didn't arrive until after six, by which time Liza had worked herself up into a fine fret, made immediately worse when he announced casually that he couldn't stay as he had an appointment. He had to go out to dinner. Liza didn't ask with whom; she imagined she knew.

'It doesn't matter,' she assured him, feigning a cool indifference, 'you don't have to explain your every movement to me. Nor can you possibly go on pretending a responsibility for an accident that was in no way your fault.'

'I think,' he said suavely, 'your words sound irritatingly familiar. Contrary to what you appear to think, I don't feel any special responsibility, Liza, but whether you're willing to admit it or not we do seem in some way involved with each other—a relationship which I would be the first to confess sometimes seems based on a mutual dislike, even distrust, but one which for me, at any rate, has its moments. Probably the day will come when we might bore each other to distraction, and then, but only then, will we say goodbye.'

Liza's throat hurt as she stared at him, and she suddenly shivered as mortification flicked sharply through her. He was annoyed, she sensed, by her impulsive and stupidly prim little speech, and was making it quite clear he wasn't prepared to put up with such schoolgirlish naïveté. His words hit hard, meant to hurt, to stimulate !

She realised this from the implacable set of his jaw, the glitter at the back of his blue eyes, but that he had succeeded in wounding her where it hurt most she tried to hide. It wasn't what he said so much—she hadn't had time to go properly into that—it was his tone, his deliberate indifference which illogically she couldn't seem to bear.

Grant's eyes were still glittering, but he seemed to achieve some kind of control, helped, perhaps unconsciously, by the pale tenseness of Liza's face. Purposefully he walked over the room and sat down, in spite of his grimness in no way like a man in any great hurry. 'You can make me some tea.' His request constituted something of a royal command and she dared not disobey.

Liza turned and walked speechlessly into the kitchenette, aware that he probably considered he had silenced her once and for all. Yet it wasn't so. She had to literally bite her lip to keep back positive floods of still-smouldering indignation. Only the too-frightening knowledge of his relentless male superiority prevented her from attacking again with an almost primitive lack of discretion.

This, and a startling awareness of what he had reduced

her to, restrained her. Yet didn't she seem to have a perfectly legitimate complaint? Hadn't Grant Latham allowed her to think they moved in similar circles, that it was quite possible for them to be friends, when in reality, they belonged to two different worlds? Did he think, she wondered, half hysterically, that her lost memory could bridge a gap which was too wide surely ever to be bridged? Not while he owned a huge business and she merely worked for him! Besides, hadn't he been out all day with another girl?

Liza's thoughts grew more and more confused as she waited sullenly for the kettle to boil, hotly resentful of a sudden that she should be suffering so acutely while the man sitting in her lounge apparently escaped unscathed. Why hadn't he ever explained the size of his 'shops'?

Her feelings could only be described as mixed, but resentment, she knew, was uppermost, even superseding misery as she returned to Grant's side with the tea. 'You don't have to stay,' she said sulkily, placing the tray with a cross little clatter on the low table before him.

When he made no reply she crouched down on a stool opposite him, grabbing the cream jug and pouring a dribble into each of their two cups. Again her manner seemed to irritate him and his mouth tightened.

'If you go on like this I'll need something stronger than tea,' he retorted at last.

She glanced at him quickly. He was still in a light grey suit which she supposed he had worn all day, and the lines deeply etched on his face managed to make him look both distant and remote, far older than he actually was, which did not help. It didn't help either that he gazed at her, his eyes narrowed and calculating, as if already he was deciding he wouldn't put up with any more of her moods. That he would only tolerate so much until she was completely well.

'Do you take sugar?' she asked, coldly, knowing perfectly that he took two lumps.

'Right,' he said, his voice very crisp as he leant forward decisively, ignoring her question, his eyes on her flushed cheeks very cool. 'You'd better get everything that's so obviously eating you off your chest!'

His short utterance struck Liza as objectionably rude and his sardonic expression told her that he had intended it should be. The slight control she had been hanging on to so tightly left her in a rush, every nerve in her body pulsing.

'You deliberately misled me.' Her eyes sparkled, a green blaze against his sombre blue.

'About the shop, you mean? Don't be an idiot.' Deliberately he held her gaze. 'You simply chose to mislead yourself. You aren't dumb exactly. All you had to do was weigh up my life-style. Besides, I thought you had a good idea?'

Again words which seemed intended to taunt! 'I did. I mean, it wasn't something that made much impression,' she said a little wildly. 'You talked of your father . . .'

'Inherited wealth, but I didn't come in for much of that, Liza. What my father left barely keeps Paula. What I have, I've worked for, and I haven't expended a great deal of time and energy just for pennies. There could be something wrong with my system that I scarcely leave myself a moment to enjoy what I make, but one day it seems conceivable I might find someone to share it with me.'

Liza flinched—someone like Davina Courtland! 'You couldn't even bear to share the knowledge that you make it with me,' she gasped. 'If Adrian hadn't hinted——'

'Liza!' Suddenly he was on his feet, his dark eyes brilliant. 'It doesn't seem as if your first day has come up to your expectations, but I'm in no way compelled to remain here, a target for your ill-humour!'

'Possibly you'll find Miss Courtland much more agreeable!' Liza, too, jumped to her feet, losing her head completely as colour flared madly across her cheekbones, her mouth trembling.

'And what do you know of Miss Courtland?' Now they were glaring at each other, the makings of a first-class argument simmering to boiling point between them.

It was Liza who looked away first. 'I'm sorry, Grant,' she

whispered, the lounge suddenly reeling, 'that was inexcusable.'

'Just so long as you realise!' he retorted furiously, and before she could stop him, he strode from the flat.

Liza collapsed in a huddled heap, and he had been gone almost ten minutes before she was aware that he had never answered her question. Nor, for that matter, had she his!

After that evening Liza didn't honestly expect to see Grant Latham again, and the misery of the night she spent ensured that she awoke next morning with eyes dark-rimmed with tears and a splitting head. Not that she was prepared to admit the true cause; a whole lot of symptoms could develop from merely a lack of sleep.

Joe came to collect her again and almost she told him to go and get lost, but immediately his cheerful smile defeated her. Joe hadn't done anything to deserve her ill-temper. Why wreak a sordid little revenge on him?

All the way to the West End, through his seemingly endless chatter, she felt odd, light-headed, a feverishness attacking her limbs which she could not account for. She hadn't been anywhere to catch a chill, yet she felt in the throes of one. Rather desperately she hoped she was mistaken. Whatever would she do if she became ill?

Suddenly, in a peculiar fashion, thoughts of the future became more worrying than those of the past. What was to become of her, a girl with no home of her own, no relations, who loved a man who disliked her? Here her thoughts floundered, becoming too painful to be tolerated. What was there about love and loving that never worked out? Hadn't she loved someone in that shrouded past? But no! Like a clearly illuminated light it came to her, the information too distinct to be mistakable. She had only loved her father!

In the nature of a physical blow the knowledge hit her, but before she could properly grasp it Joe was announcing, as he had done yesterday, that they had arrived. With dazed eyes Liza gazed about her, scarcely hearing, only seeing her father and—that girl! She remembered completely then, and flinched sickeningly from the pain of it, an almost visible shudder running through her.

'I say, miss, are you all right?' Joe's quick voice held a hint of sharp concern as the lift carried them upwards and he noticed her white face.

'Why, yes...' Liza's face was suddenly brighter as she discovered, in that moment, that she was indeed all right! Shaken, but not utterly devastated, as she had feared to be by the total recall of an incident which, even before the fire, she had always remembered with shock.

It didn't seem possible, but it was true. In the space of seconds a miracle seemed to have happened, bringing with it a new sense of peace. And miraculously it remained, even when she could still see an upturned boat and hear the gentle voice of the Embassy official who had informed her of the two bodies washed up on the beach. It all came back, but it did not hurt any more, because with it came the sure knowledge that her father would not have wanted to live without the woman he loved.

Her mind full of this, and the wonder of feeling her own grief and jealousy dissolving, Liza had no time to piece anything else together before they arrived at the department. This, she saw immediately, was busy.

Miss Russell was nowhere to be seen and Chloe rushed forward in a flurry. 'One hell of a morning!' she hissed loudly, catching sight of Liza emerging from the lift. 'Among other things, which I've no time to explain, three of the girls are off and I've two ladies, both in a hurry, in my fitting rooms. Do get a move on, Dean, get rid of your coat and give me a hand. Old Russell's in a flat spin!'

She's not the only one, Liza reflected briefly, as she tried to hurry, her fingers seeming all thumbs as she struggled with zips and fumbled with buttons. Though why Miss Russell should be distracted she had no idea. For the next hour Liza kept more than busy; she ran, deliberately seeking to submerge her new awareness in work, beating back memories that attempted to crowd in on her, stretched on a limb, it seemed, between panic and curiosity.

That book in the library at Lynsend must have been one of her father's! Wouldn't it be nice to be able to tell Adrian that he too had been quite a well-known writer, if of a

different kind? Her father's books would never have made
him affluent, not even if he'd lived for another fifty years.

Adrian ... Thinking about him offered, in some inexplicable way, some release, if only because it enabled her
not to dwell on anyone else. But didn't she and Adrian have
more in common than she had imagined before her memory
returned? Hadn't she done more or less what Adrian had
done after a bereavement? She had allowed shock to take
over, turned her back on the world, rushed away from
everything and everyone she had ever known to take the
first job she found. Not that she remembered having any
specific training for any particular career. Just odd things
like being able to sail a boat in foreign waters, typing and
translating, an aptitude to settle down and make a temporary home where none existed. Yet such accomplishments
didn't usually carry special qualifications and she must have
been lucky to have found this job in a store like Lathams
where most of the staff had acquired a very high standard
of training.

Abstractedly unaware that in spite of her endeavours, her
thoughts were unconsciously taking over, Liza left a cubicle
with a pile of models over her arm. Her customer, a charming young woman, had been very easy to deal with, and
Liza felt thrilled that she had sold her first three dresses.
But the warmth of her satisfaction in no way prepared her
for the man who strode swiftly into the department. A man
who was obviously in a hurry and—a temper! As he bore
ruthlessly down on a flustered Miss Russell he failed immediately to notice Liza, but she saw him.

Shocked to a sudden standstill, her eyes darkening with a
terrifying dismay, Liza stared at Grant Latham, her whole
being submerged by a positive cataclysm of disbelief. With
a speed of transition which drove the breath from her body
she hurtled back through time and space to another moment weeks ago when he had strode into this very department in exactly the same way, on his face the same expression of furious impatience!

'Oh, no!' Liza wasn't aware she had spoken aloud until
he turned abruptly, obviously overhearing.

'Liza!' In two strides he was beside her, just as he had been on that other day, and she had done then, she knew she hated him. On that other day he had openly attacked her with scarcely any justification at all, and it had been the first time she had seen him!

'Oh, no . . .' This time her exclamation was merely a horrified whisper as everything went momentarily black and she swayed on her feet.

The world about her rocking crazily, Liza dropped the gowns she was carrying and clutched wildly at a nearby counter, attempting to save herself. She missed the counter, but Grant Latham reached her just in time, whipping her quickly into his arms, taking no notice of the startled gasps around him as he strode with Liza into Miss Russell's office.

'I'm quite all right,' she protested.

'You don't look it.' Taking no more notice of her feeble protests than he had of the women outside, he lowered her carefully into Miss Russell's chair, and, obviously aware of that bewildered lady fluttering behind him, demanded brandy.

'At once!' It was a terse command which Miss Russell didn't pretend to misunderstand. Liza watched, dazed, frozenly aware that Miss Russell found some immediately.

'Get one of the girls to bring Miss Dean's coat,' Grant added as he personally administered the brandy, completely disregarding Liza's feeble protests. 'I'll take her home straight away,' he added curtly. 'It's quite obvious she's been doing too much.'

'Why—sir!' Miss Russell's eyes widened with not unreasonable indignation.

'I've done scarcely anything,' Liza felt forced to fly to Miss Russell's defence. 'It wasn't that.'

'Shut up!' Now that he saw a little colour returning to Liza's cheeks he was equally brusque with her. As Liza subsided, solely because she suddenly felt too ill to argue, Grant spoke again to Miss Russell. 'I believe my stepmother is around somewhere. It appears she's making a brief visit to Town. If by any chance she's looking for me

will you kindly tell her I've been called away.' Without
telling her where I am—the glance he levelled at Miss
Russell clearly added what he did not say.

Poor Paula, Liza sighed dejectedly, as Grant drove her
home. Hadn't he been cross with Paula, too, that day in the
store before the fire?

Shortly afterwards they arrived at the flat. Grant was
apparently still not aware that Liza now regarded him as a
stranger, that now she understood their relative positions
and realised they could have little more to say to each other.

Glancing at him quickly, Liza decided that it was a most
peculiar feeling. It was as if he were two men, one she
disliked intensely, as if the weeks since her accident had
never been, and one whom she had come to l——

But no, not even to herself could she ever admit the
extent of her own folly. Better by far to concentrate on her
hate and forget the rest.

Fervently, as Grant closed the door of the flat, she regretted leaving the store. There, at least, she might have
been comparatively safe, not exposed and vulnerable as she
felt now.

Grant, however, seemed disinclined to give her time to
mull over anything. He glanced at her sideways, unsmiling
as he dragged her ruthlessly over to the window, and turned
her face to the light, his fingers steely with strength beneath
her chin. 'So you remember?' he demanded tightly, asking,
when she nodded numbly, 'Everything?'

What purpose would it serve to be evasive? 'Yes,' her
voice shook, 'going to work this morning, it came back to
me properly about my father. Then finally, when you
arrived in the department . . .'

Curtly he inquired, 'You remembered we had never met,
not properly?'

Again the helpless nod of her head, her eyes darkly shadowed, full of a distress which was beginning to show. 'You
were furious with me that day. You must believe me. It was
so apparent that Miss Russell lectured me for ages and
made me work during lunch. That was how I discovered
the fire . . .'

'So you see it was my fault.'

'Yes. At least,' she amended, trying painfully to be honest, 'I suppose it's something that happens all the time, and the fire couldn't possibly have been foreseen; but don't you understand, we must take up where we left off, and we didn't even like each other.'

Grant's face took on its usual formidable mask and he sighed roughly. 'You can't wipe out the intervening weeks, Liza, nor am I going to let you. And, contrary to what you might think, I'm glad your memory has returned. I won't have to treat you with kid gloves any more, which has been quite a strain, if you did but know it.'

His eyes held hers, very dark and challenging, as if he was aware of something she was not. There was something in his narrowed glance and the tightening of his firm mouth to make her stomach quake, to bring tiny beads of perspiration to her already hot brow. Silently, unable to answer him, her lips quivered.

Immediately, as if it came to him that he was perhaps driving her a bit too far, too quickly, his hand eased a little on the tender skin of her throat. 'Maybe I could be gentle with you,' he muttered, his meaning far from clear as he stared at her, as if he would like to uncover all her secrets, lay bare all her thoughts!

Drawing her back across the room, he pushed her down to the settee, his hard face showing a flicker of compassion. 'Sit there,' he said softly. 'This time I'll make the tea. Then we must talk.'

Minutes later, after swallowing the hot, sweet liquid, Liza felt some of her inner tension fading, and when Grant told her he was taking her along to his doctor for an immediate check-up she didn't protest too much.

'But I'm sure I shall be quite all right now,' she assured him, 'there's really no need to go to all this trouble. I've no more problems.'

He shot her a swiftly calculating glance, his face dryly mocking as he sat down beside her. 'You could still have some, if of a different kind, but it seems sensible to make sure the medical ones, at least, are out of the way.'

His meaning wasn't exactly clear and she felt an odd reluctance to ask him to explain, and the long level look he gave her didn't seem to supply any of the right answers. If it wasn't so crazy she might almost have taken notice of that growing suspicion within her, that he regarded her more in the light of a defaulter, who should be ready and willing to pay for her crimes.

'If you're talking about this flat,' she said quickly, 'I won't need it any longer.'

'I wasn't,' he replied reasonably. 'Besides, your landlady will still be away.'

'When will she be back?'

'Leave it alone, Liza!'

Impatience tinged his voice again, daring Liza to say more. Nervously resentful she bit her lip, not wholly acquiescent. She could always make her own arrangements. She might even decide to stay here if she could afford to, but there would be her personal belongings to collect.

'While we're on the subject,' she heard Grant continue, 'where did you live before you came to work for me?'

She named an island in the West Indies.

'You liked it there?'

'Yes...' Suddenly it seemed the most natural thing in the world to be telling him how she and her father had lived. For a little while, it seemed, she was able to put her antagonism to one side as she told him of the many places they had visited. If the man who listened intently was aware that she barely mentioned this last island, Liza failed to notice.

'I've read some of your father's books,' he commented, 'Quite engrossing. Graham Dean—I might have guessed.'

'You have?' Liza's face quivered slightly, though whether from pleasure or pain it was difficult to say.

He nodded lightly. In contrast his voice was almost brutal. 'Didn't you find the shop a bit tame after leading such a permissive life? Your poor father must have had his hands full.'

'Permissive?'

'One would naturally describe it thus.' There was a faint

violence in his sardonic tones, mocking the startled query in a pair of wide green eyes fixed suddenly on his face.

'No!' Yet unexpectedly she flushed. 'I suppose there was a certain amount of freedom,' she admitted.

There came a second's pause and she wondered why he should look so grim. Grant Latham, she suspected, might be inclined towards permissiveness himself, given the place and opportunity! But no, both those, to him, would be minor details which he would provide himself. His actions were always deliberate, he would never leave anything to chance. Not as lesser mortals must often do! So why should he sit in judgment on her father, who Liza could scarcely ever remember looking at a woman since her mother died? Not until...

Abruptly, obviously cutting back a further comment, Grant asked, 'How did your father die?'

Her hesitation was easily perceptible, as was the clenching of her hands. 'He was drowned,' she answered starkly.

Grant Latham's eyebrows rose in unspoken query.

His hard persistence brought pain, hardening her own voice with dislike while it paled her skin, and muddling the explanation she gave only reluctantly. 'He had a shock, and this sudden squall blew up. A kind of miniature cyclone, which can be pretty devastating out there. There are warnings, of course, and it's fairly safe if one uses common sense...'

'This shock your father received?' Grant pressed.

A shock of nerves cut through her like a lance, tearing her apart, and she knew she could not tell him. He might never understand and she couldn't bear to risk it. The possible tarnishing of her father's name she could never consider. No one knew, not even on the island had other people known for sure. Just the doctor ... Tomorrow she must go back to her old room and destroy the diaries. It was something she ought to have done before, only they had seemed her last link with everything she had once held so dear.

'Liza!'

The sharpness in Grant's voice prompted cruelly, as if he considered her silence constituted almost—a declaration of

some kind of guilt? Liza, looking away from his per-
plexingly contemptuous face, found herself murmuring unhappily, 'I'm sorry, Mr Latham, it's something I'd rather
not talk about.'

His smile was far from pleasant, but this time, to Liza's
relief, he didn't persist. There was even a flicker of humour
to curve his decisive mouth as she stared at him blindly.
'We can't go back, Liza, you know that, so I'm afraid you
must drop the *Mr Latham*.'

Her head lifted at that, instantly defiant, her eyes suddenly full of resentment, blazing like those of a highly
strung small cat. 'I can't!'

He smouldered then, diverted by her fury, and she knew
right away what he referred to. 'You stood there, a flaming
redhead in more ways than one, and I was immediately
attracted. So you see, my dear Liza, you can't possibly
just—drop me!'

'Why ever not?' she challenged, recklessly disregarding
the warning glitter in his eyes, not caring for his threatening tones at all.

'Not if you value your job.'

Silken his voice now, a sneer of triumph in it, indicating
clearly that he considered he had the upper hand! And
hadn't he? 'You wouldn't dare,' she breathed, 'oh, please
not!'

That dare was a mistake. He leant nearer, merely looking
at her. 'Would I not?'

'You drive a hard bargain!'

'You might not do so badly out of it yourself.'

It was all beyond her. Annoyed by some hidden meaning
she couldn't follow, Liza's anger turned to weary petulance.
'Oh, Grant, it's not possible to continue our relationship as
it has been over the past few weeks.'

'You should know that,' he agreed.

'Well then,' she stared at him uncertainly, 'I'm glad you
see.'

'I see nothing of the sort.' His eyes hardened to a blue
flint. 'Do you imagine I have the time or patience to start
from the beginning again? I'm no young lad, Liza, willing

to sing beneath your window each evening!'

'No Romeo,' she breathed, completely unnerved.

'Nor would you make a very successful Juliet.'

'It's still impossible! There's nothing between us...'

'Prove it!' His voice was laced with smooth confidence, his face, steel-like and alert as he moved nearer to her, overlaid by a wholly masculine impatience. His eyes glittered over her without their usual detachment as he reached out, pulling her into his arms, while a muscle jerked demandingly at the side of his mouth. 'I said prove it,' he repeated, his gaze fixed now, and unrelenting, on her flushed face, her tremulous, shaking mouth.

CHAPTER TEN

'DON'T you see,' Grant said softly, minutes later, 'how impossible it would be to go back to that first day in the store?'

His arms, which held her unresistingly to him, tightened, and his voice flicked her like the touch of a whip. Liza's head spun, her hands clenching with compulsive little movements against the back of his neck as she tried to look away from the hard dark face so near her own.

Something very strange was happening to her. At the touch of his lips white-hot flames were shooting along her veins, so relentlessly that nowhere could she find any breath with which to protest. His image possessed her mind to the point of pain, refusing to fade merely because the past had returned to haunt her, and the strange magnetism between them seemed, if anything, stronger.

'Grant.' Impossible to speak clearly. She could only go on staring up at him, her hair spilling about her flushed cheeks in wild disorder, her eyes, the slumbrous green pupils clouding the white, reflecting all her inner torments. 'What do you intend doing with me?' she breathed at last, her voice a strangled whisper from a too tense throat.

His laughter was low, his eyes suddenly brilliant with a triumph he took little trouble to hide. 'You'll just have to give yourself a little time to find out,' he replied enigmatically, taking in his hand a thick swathe of hair, drawing it under her chin so that her lips tilted up to meet his mouth. 'Maybe a few clues like this could supply the answer.'

There was a leap within her like a primitive fear as his head bent, as she heard the deep intake of his breath as his

mouth once again met her own with practised precision.
The hand twisting her hair so tightly firmed about her
vulnerable throat, taking her head hard back into the curve
of his shoulder so that she couldn't escape and he kissed her
unwilling mouth until it softened and parted beneath his
and she lay spent and breathless in his arms.

'Grant...' Softly she spoke his name, and this time it
was she who was breathing deeply, her mouth very sensuous, seeking his again, her slender young body, warm and
smoothly alive, pressed against him. One of her hands left
his shoulders to slide beneath his jacket, as if eager to feel
the strength of the hard, masculine muscles under his taut
skin. She felt wholly awakened with a burning, intoxicating
sweetness that searched, even while it wished to give and
give. She seemed caught in the quicksand of her own in-
articulate excitement, all kinds of notions filtering madly
through her brain. Her long curling lashes fluttered from off
hot cheeks as her eyes opened to stare unseeingly, like a
sleepwalker's, straight into his, aware only of a frightening
desire to be as close to him as she could get.

But it was not to be as simple as that. He had the
advantage, and the narrowing of his watchful eyes declared
that he knew it, but this was neither the time nor place. A
predator might corner its prey, but a man like Grant
Latham had learnt long ago that there was little real
pleasure to be derived from haste. That he understood the
state of her shattered senses was made plain by the way his
hand moved gently to the lovely curve of her breast, but
apart from that his face remained curiously empty, enigmatic.

It was Liza's frustration, not his, that brought forth the
unconsciously impulsive words. She felt his hand, his touch
bringing her to breaking point, somewhere between
pleasure and pain. 'You don't want me any more!'

His eyes glittered at a statement so rash, so wildly un-
restrained. 'God knows I want you all right!' his voice was
terse, as if suddenly, in spite of his years of experience, he
was having to put a tight rein on himself. 'Don't provoke
me, little one, you're not dealing with any unfledged boy.'

'So you keep telling me!' She drew a half hysterical breath, her eyes enormous with hidden strain, as if she sensed his inner rejection and did not like it. 'You started this,' she accused him, feeling absolutely as childish of a sudden as he made her out to be.

'Guilty, then,' he acknowledged, his transition to cool indifference perplexing to Liza's devastated mind. 'Come on.' Completely in charge of the situation, he rose to his feet, drawing an unsteady Liza up with him. 'Go and comb your hair while I ring your doctor. Then I'll take you out to lunch. Afterwards I'm sure you'll feel better.'

The change in his manner from a determined lover to something very remotely detached was stunning: Paling, she gazed up at him, all her uncertainties blazing in her eyes for him to see. 'I couldn't go out, I couldn't eat a thing,' she said helplessly.

'You can, and you will,' he smiled darkly. 'Run along now and do as I say.'

Liza was still brooding about it over two weeks later when again she was dressing, this time to go out with Grant for dinner. When he liked he could be extremely domineering and there was no gainsaying him, but it was not, she tried to tell herself, something she enjoyed. He had taken her out to lunch that day and personally escorted her to see her doctor, seeking, it seemed, to be reassured that she was completely recovered.

'Excellent,' the doctor had exclaimed, apparently well satisfied, even while he had made Liza promise to see him again. 'Not that there's any great need,' he promised her, 'just as long as you take it relatively easy until you're certain yourself that everything is as it should be.'

All of which should have proved very satisfactory to a girl who had only been longing to be well, and the continuing feeling of unhappiness within her she couldn't understand. Surely she ought to be getting used to being without her father, to be learning to forget his involvement with that girl? Thinking of this had brought back to mind her diaries which would undoubtedly be in her old rooms, to which she still held a key. At the first opportunity she had returned and found them, bringing them back here to read, but there had been nothing in the closely written pages she hadn't remembered, nothing that she could blame for her unremitting depression. She had intended to destroy the diaries. Instead she had hidden them carefully in her bedroom, not able to bring herself to break with what seemed her last link with the past.

The problem of whether or not to keep her old rooms also continued to bother her. Chloe had begged to be allowed to have them as it would mean she hadn't so far to travel to work, but as yet Liza was undecided, although she realised she could not go on paying two rents indefinitely. If both rents hadn't been so modest she could not have done it at all. Her present flat seemed to present an irresistible temptation. She was fast growing used to its luxury, but there was something about it that could still bring a surge of uneasiness.

It was surprising how quickly she had fallen into the regular routine of the store. Amazing how she sometimes felt the intervening weeks might never have been, how she had sometimes almost to pinch herself to convince herself they had actually happened. Even Miss Russell's manner had returned to a more normal level, even if she still seemed to treat Liza occasionally with a rather puzzling amount of consideration, not usually shown to such young members of the staff.

Liza had been sent along to have her hair properly trimmed and set, and now her head shone with beautiful glowing tints, complementing her flawless complexion. The other girls said she hadn't changed, only improved, but Liza was aware that outward appearances didn't tell the whole story. Inside she felt very different; for one thing, she was in love. After that morning when Grant had held her in his arms she could never deny it, although she had no idea if he shared her symptoms. Somehow she very much doubted it, in spite of the fact that she saw him almost continually. Her own feelings, where he was concerned, often alarmed her, but she had had no means of knowing whether he shared any such degree of sensitivity.

Since that morning when her memory had fully returned Grant hadn't kissed her again, although she saw him almost every evening and he quite often rang her before she went to work, sometimes taking her there himself. Liza could not decide whether his former vigilance had formed a habit he did not bother to break, but, bemused by a growing desire to be near him, she shrank from probing too closely. As to his demands on her free time, she found she couldn't resist him; even to look at him was to be swept into an abyss, lost.

She felt oddly thankful that he very rarely came near her department at the store, and if anyone suspected anything nothing was said. Chloe, however, had been greatly put out when Liza had refused to see a film at the Odeon with her.

'You can't stay in every evening,' she had protested, frowning. 'If you won't come out shall I come round? I'd be company.'

When Liza, rather miserably, had been forced to confess that she had a prior engagement, Chloe had been full of curiosity, which had quickly turned to disdain when Liza refused to explain whom it was with. 'Oh, keep your little secrets!' she had retorted sharply, turning away.

Chloe hadn't been exactly friendly since, and Liza missed her spontaneous chatter. Yet how could she have told Chloe about Grant when there was nothing really to tell, and such a disclosure, along with the ensuing gossip, might only have caused him undue embarrassment.

If Chloe's dissatisfaction caused Liza some unhappiness, an unexpected and wholly surprising visit from Paula Latham had been responsible for much more. Paula had been waiting at the flat on Liza's first half day off and had begged her to return to Lynsend to work for Adrian.

'He hasn't done anything since you left,' Paula had explained to an apprehensive Liza. 'I had hoped to see you when you first left Lynsend and returned to the shop, but Grant put me off. He doesn't know I'm here today.'

'But I couldn't.' In the face of Paula's determination it had been very hard to refuse. Liza had swallowed hard, not caring for the expression of despair on Paula's usually indifferent face. 'Besides,' she had added, inconsequently, 'Lynsend belongs to Grant.'

Paula hadn't followed her turn of thought, nor had she appeared to try, but she had said surprisingly, 'Grant has made Lynsend over to me for my lifetime, then it goes to Adrian, so that problem doesn't exist any longer.'

Liza had blinked, her bewilderment growing. 'That wasn't quite what I meant,' she had said miserably. She knew that what Paula suggested was not possible, but aware that Paula must have been something more than desperate to have come to her like this, she had tried to be helpful. 'While you're in town, if you went to one of the bureaux, I'm sure they would find you someone much more capable than me.'

'But he only wants you!' Paula had cried, almost pathetic in her sudden vulnerability. 'Unless you come I don't know what I shall do!'

'I'm sorry.' Liza's discomfort had grown. She had also felt vaguely sorry for Paula and found it hard not to allow herself to be persuaded. 'Don't you see,' she had tried to point out feebly, and regarding her own position with Grant perhaps ridiculously, 'it doesn't do to become too dependent on any one person. If I've proved that Adrian still has some inclination to write, it shouldn't then be so impossible to find another girl with the same potentiality.'

She had taken great pains in trying to persuade Paula this could be so, but Paula had been far from convinced. She had only left after Liza had agreed to contact her should she ever change her mind. 'But it could be an empty promise,' Liza had cautioned her anxiously, dismayed by a new warmth in the woman's smile.

Liza hadn't told Grant about Paula's visit, for two reasons—the first because Paula had asked her rather nervously not to, and, secondly because she hadn't thought it worthwhile. As she had no intention of working for Adrian there didn't seem much point. Liza had known with growing conviction, these past few days, that at some time in the immediate future she must change her job, but going to work for Adrian might merely aggravate her present position, and increase the problems she already had.

Sighing, she turned now from an unseeing contemplation of her reflection in the mirror to struggle with the intricacies of a too-tight zip. One deeply indrawn breath later, the operation completed, she reached quickly for the lovely container of exotic perfume which Grant had given her the evening before. She hadn't tried it until now and it smelt delicious, even if slightly wicked, surrounding her as it did with a fragrantly sensuous aroma.

They were going to a concert, then on somewhere to eat and dance, and Liza had been looking forward to it intensely. Until she had started thinking about Paula, and admitted the insidious effect Paula was having on her conscience. Twice since her visit Paula had telephoned, and each time Liza had found it increasingly difficult not to give her the answer she so obviously hoped for.

The doorbell rang, swiftly imperious, and there wasn't time for Liza to arrange her hair in the sophisticated style she had had in mind. She was forced to make do with leaving it loose, a cloud of burnished red-gold about her shoulders. Doubtfully she flicked a swift glance in the glass. It seemed to provide too great a contrast to her dress, a beautiful if rather sophisticated model in an unusual, very flattering shade of green which, owing to an unnoticeable flaw in the skirt, Miss Russell had offered her cheaply. Liza hadn't been aware that the décolleté was so low until she had it on, and saw how it left so much of her shoulders and neck bare.

Biting her lip uncertainly, she considered her reflection, but it wasn't possible to change now, not with the doorbell ringing again impatiently. Quickly she slung her fur cape around her, hiding the provocative cut of the softly glittering bodice before she ran to let Grant in.

The evening, as all such evenings did in Grant's company, passed, at least to begin with, with comparative ease. The concert Liza loved and because she found the music incredibly relaxing, she realised how tense she had become of late. Afterwards in the vestibule groups were forming and people spoke to Grant, looking inquiringly at Liza, who didn't know how her wonderful young beauty aroused curiosity.

Grant didn't seem inclined to linger and apart from a brief nod here and there made no attempt to engage anyone in conversation. He swept her along, allowing no hesitation, a world of sudden purpose betrayed by the adamant set of his jawline.

The place he chose for supper had a much livelier atmosphere than the softly enchanting one of the theatre, and Liza was aware that unreasonably she resented such an abrupt intrusion on her still dreaming senses. In the theatre she had seemed alone with Grant, secluded in a world of their own. Here, the general air of gaiety intruded to a far greater degree.

They ate, Liza not really able to recall doing so, so conscious was she of the man, darkly elegant, superbly in control of everything, by her side. Too controlled? Liza shivered, reacting compulsively, with a lack of restraint Grant seemed never to permit himself, as later they danced together. His dark head bent to her fair one, his eyes caressing her soft skin, the swirling glory of her hair.

'I'm enchanted by your dress,' he murmured with commendable ingenuity, as she arched delicate brows at his deliberate survey, pretending a sophistication she barely possessed. 'It's a charming scrap of material, anyway,' he teased, his smile deepening with some satisfaction as she flushed charmingly.

He gave her no opportunity to reply as the beat of the music changed and he whirled her closer. 'You're so light on your feet, you appear to have rhythm in your very bones. I wonder what else you have?' he breathed, his lips moving with a remembered insistence against her ear.

Liza's heart raced, quick, nervous thuds which she was terrified he would hear. He had drawn her very close. Now he held her away from him, the easier to glance down at her once more.

'There's an irresistible little pulse going mad at the base of your throat,' he noted outrageously. 'Could it have anything to do with me?'

His night-shaded eyes glinted, and she ought to have denied such a taunting remark and pulled away. There was that within her that urged her to rush back to the safer precincts of their table, but she had reckoned without the dictates of her own body.

'It could have.' The admission escaped, a mere thread of unconscious sound he bent nearer to catch, and her green eyes, intensely lovely, fell before his glittering gaze.

'You like me?' His voice compelled an answer, and she was caught in a whirlpool of her own heightened senses. She might evade him with her eyes, but no other way.

'Sometimes I love you,' she vowed helplessly, her breathless confession supported by the almost visible throbbing of a totally disorganised heart.

'And she chooses such a place to tell me!' His grasp tightened with punishing intent. 'I'm not quite an expert on such matters, but I believe there are better spots for such confessions. Shall we go home?'

Whether it was a question or a command, Liza wasn't sure. 'No,' she shivered, submerged suddenly in a saving flood of self-preservation, 'I'm still hungry.'

'So'm I,' Grant muttered darkly, 'but for different things.'

Nonetheless he did prove he was not a man in a hurry, willing to acknowledge, if with a slightly inscrutable smile, that they were only half way through their meal. The undisputable fact that Liza's appetite had obviously left her seemed merely to add to his enigmatic satisfaction.

Liza, for her part, with slightly more control over her wayward emotions, talked quickly, unaware that her swift chatter reflected her inner turmoil very clearly. If she laughed too often, trying to make light of her absurd indiscretions, he appeared in no way convinced, continuing to watch her with a faintly tolerant impatience.

It was something of a relief when, some time after midnight, she could eventually decide that he was bored by her rather trite remarks, the cool impassiveness of his expression happily displacing her former uncertainty. Yet she wasn't incautious.

'I'm tired,' she murmured, after suggesting they left. 'You could always just drop me off. I think I shall go straight to bed.'

He glanced at her then, but there was nothing to imply in his lazy smile that he found her naïve. He simply nodded, and proceeded with the usual ritual of signalling for the bill before reaching for her cape which he dropped protectively about her shoulders. One hand he swept around her slender neck, releasing her caught hair in an oddly intimate gesture, more disturbing than his lack of words had ever been.

A few minutes later they were on their way, speeding homewards through the night through wind-blown and frost-cooled streets. For once Liza felt really glad of the extravagant central heating in her flat as Grant inserted the key and swung open the door, pushing her gently inside. He had all the demeanour of a man who knows exactly what he is doing, but she didn't realise this until she turned innocently to wish him goodnight. By then the door was closed, and he wasn't on the outside!

The hours before had only been a beginning.

'Liza,' he said, as her whole body stiffened as if forced to make some kind of protest. Was she so helpless? Had she made an irredeemable mistake in over-estimating the strength of her own defences, so that she could only stare at him in a trance when he advanced towards her, removing the coat she clasped so protectively in taut fingers, before gathering her wordlessly to him?

He lifted her, carrying her through the small hall into the dimly lit lounge, and placed her very gently on the wide sofa. Abruptly he came upright, slipping off his jacket and releasing the top buttons of his restricting silk shirt, then dropped down beside her.

'Come here,' he pulled her straight into his arms, holding her still, not prepared to countenance any further opposition as his fingers traced the curve of her neck while her eyes clung to him with a kind of confused mesmerisation.

Liza's body began responding for her, wreathed in flames, yielding to the insistence of his caressing hands.

'Kiss me,' she whispered, forgetting she hadn't wanted him here at all, entirely at the mercy of her own untried emotions.

His mouth was ecstasy. He drew her very close until her soft slender body yielded wholly against him, and he kissed her with extreme passion, his arms hard and compelling, holding her to him, forcing her to respond with a violence of feeling she had not known she possessed. There was no holding back, nor did she want to. If she unconsciously sensed that he constituted an active danger, she also knew she owed him more than she could ever repay in any other way—that she could deny him nothing.

As the pressure of his lips increased, her fingers went urgently to his face, taking a sensuous pleasure in the feel of his hard skin where his shirt parted at the neck, and as his own hand swept the narrow straps of her dress aside, there was only the bare urgency of an overwhelming desire between them.

'Liza.' His mouth lifted from her throbbing lips to trail down her throat, to softly arouse her in other ways which she knew nothing about. His hands hurt with an intensity of probing and a soft moan escaped her lips as she turned to him completely, clinging, wildly responsive, her arms tight against the hard demanding muscles of his back.

Then his mouth was on hers again and there was no sound, only the heavy pounding of her frightened heart.

'I'll be good to you, darling, you won't have anything to regret.' His voice was thick against her parted lips, his mouth moving softly over hers as a mutual ardour linked them with growing warmth and power. Patterns of light fell on her still, pale face, her eyes closed against the unbearable longing, the feverish heat of her own trembling limbs.

'Grant ...' she moaned, her mouth reluctant to leave his for even a moment, wanting him so badly and not trying to hide it. With her eyes tightly closed, her arms warmly clinging, she didn't care if he knew it, or of the consequences.

His hesitation was fractional but it was there, a fine barrier he was in no way inclined to allow. 'You fully realise what could happen?'

'I love you—love you.' It was a glorious declaration, which she could never hold back. Nothing to be ashamed of, but something to be confessed with an intensity of feeling!

'As much as you loved that other man?'

A lightning quiver shook Liza violently. It was a question she could never have foreseen, striking her like an icy blast, cooling her young, unguarded ardour as nothing else might have done. Grant Latham's voice was suddenly terse, as if the query had been wrung from him in spite of himself. Normally a woman's other affairs would not have bothered him unduly.

'What other man?' Apprehension coloured Liza's face and she could scarcely bear to look at him. Her eyes darkened, the first fleeting coolness of imminent disaster imbuing her tones with an odd bewilderment. Her body tensed as a subconscious fear rapidly dispersed her headlong impulsiveness. 'Grant!' she cried wildly, as he didn't speak, 'who are you talking about?' His grimness was suddenly terrible, as was his hidden accusation.

'Oh, come,' he said, his glance going over her with a derisive weariness, 'you don't have to lie to me any more. When you first insisted on coming back to London, I went over your old room, merely to assure myself there wasn't anything there to alarm you. I found your diary, read the last page. No more, but it was enough,' his mouth tightened. 'You said the child was lost and you were heartbroken. You even named the man.'

He couldn't! It wasn't possible that Grant had read that! Horrified, Liza could only stare, with what seemed like guilt written all over her. And Grant thought . . . Oh, no, she couldn't possibly let him! Yet how could she betray her father? How could she ever begin to tell him about her father and that girl?

She couldn't even consider talking about it, although the bitterness had long since left. No, it was much better that

Grant should believe what he did of her. It might mean heartbreak, but he had never meant to marry her. What he had proposed this evening had been something less than that!

A terrible shame suddenly flooded Liza's heart as she thought despairingly of her own response, but it did inadvertently supply the strength to pull herself from his arms, to push him away. 'I'm sorry, Grant,' her great green eyes were glazed with frantic shock, 'it would be better if you left now—I can't explain.'

'You mean you don't want to!' From an ardent lover, prepared to accept her on any terms, his voice was full of hard dislike which would have precluded any sort of relationship. He made no attempt to detain her or to touch her again. His eyes were bleak, as he reached for his jacket and stood staring at her coldly. 'It ought to cheer me up that there was at least one man who didn't believe that aura of young innocence. I was crazy to imagine I could take advantage of it, too, but somehow I haven't the stomach for it!'

'Grant!'

'Goodbye, Liza Dean. Happy hunting!' His grim inflexibility hit her, bringing her almost to fainting point as, with one last contemptuous glance, he strode savagely from the flat. As the door slammed she collapsed in a crumpled heap on the sofa, where only so short a time ago she had known such rapture.

Liza made no effort to go to bed, remaining where she was on the sofa where she must have fallen into an exhausted sleep, drugged by tears which couldn't seem to stop falling. There were dreams, too, of being held in Grant's arms, and when she awoke she was trembling, her head aching so hard that she was forced to seek her aspirin bottle.

She had no really clear idea of what she was going to do after she left Latham's. Leave there she must, but she also knew she must go and finish the week, give proper notice. Everyone had been so kind, she couldn't possibly just walk out, and as she had no qualms about seeing Grant again, there was no excuse for not doing the right thing.

She could, though, leave this flat immediately. There was nothing to stop her settling on the way out and returning to her old rooms that evening. All her possessions could be packed in one small suitcase—the clothes Grant had supplied her with she didn't want to see again. If she hurried, and it was only after eight, she could drop her case off on the way to work. The landlady might not be back yet, but she had a key and would manage somehow.

Grant she tried to shut out completely, as even to think of him for a moment brought a renewed trickle of tears. A trickle that threatened to turn into a veritable flood when she considered what his opinion of her over the last few weeks must have been. Now she knew she hadn't merely imagined the coldness of his attitude on occasion!

There was some consolation in knowing she hated him because he had so swiftly misjudged her, had decided to settle for a sordid affair. Perhaps her own actions had not been entirely blameless, but she had never been guilty of the wild indiscretions he attributed to her. Chance might have been a fine thing, Liza thought bitterly, but considering the close surveillance her father had kept over her, she had had very little of that.

Down in the entrance hall, in the office, another shock awaited her. As it was so early the usual woman was not on duty, and when Liza offered the stranger who was there her few pounds for the month's rent, the girl stared incredulously.

'There must be some mistake, Miss Dean. That amount wouldn't cover a week!'

'Then how much?' Liza's lips were stiff, and she didn't care what the girl thought. The sum named stunned her. 'Are you sure?' she gasped.

'Certain,' the girl considered her newly painted fingernails, indifferent to Liza's alarm. 'I've worked here since the flats were built.'

Somehow she would repay Grant, Liza vowed, but she would never forgive him!

By the time she reached the store her head was aching

again, and she was too numb with extreme exhaustion to feel any sort of reaction when she was told by a busy Miss Russell that Mr Latham wanted to see her immediately she came in.

'Yes, Miss Russell,' Liza said, and went and spent ten minutes in a distant cloakroom.

When she returned to the department, Miss Russell, not aware of Liza's deception, smiled vaguely, gave her a routine task to complete, and nothing more was said. Grant, Liza supposed, would be busy and forget he hadn't seen her. He wouldn't realise she was one step ahead, and had no desire to listen to his personal dismissal of her services. This evening she would simply tell Miss Russell she could stay no longer—then go!

She kept busy, feverishly so, giving herself no time to ponder on what had been or what might have been, and the small commotion at the other end of the department seemed no justification to remove her eyes from the customer she was attending. Miss Russell's voice at her elbow consequently startled.

'You told me you had seen Mr Latham?'

'I didn't—at least, not in actual words, you merely assumed . . .' Horrified, Liza's voice trailed off. She had been in no way prepared to find Mr Latham standing directly behind Miss Russell's rigid shoulder.

'You can come with me immediately, Liza. Miss Russell will see to everything here.'

'But, sir!' Again Liza's voice failed her. When she was very young and had been told to do something she would rather not, she had sometimes screamed and dug her heels in, and been excused on account of her red hair. One glance at Grant Latham's forbidding face, however, warned her the same tactics wouldn't work with him! But did he have to make things so unpleasant for her? Miss Russell was obviously annoyed, though she did her best to hide it behind a forced smile, and Liza felt in no fit state to face the interview he so obviously had in mind. Segments of what he had overlooked to mention last night, she supposed, a saving anger lifting her chin to a healthier angle as with a half-bitten-off exclamation he placed a relentless hand beneath her arm and whipped her along to his office.

He gave her no opportunity to continue her faltering protest. It was all she could do to keep her eyes lowered in order to avoid the many curious glances as she stumbled blindly by his side. Once in his office he immediately closed the door, but instead of letting her go he kept his hand on her arm, his other hand coming up to whirl her around to face him, holding her even more tightly. In spite of herself Liza felt her heart hammering wildly, and the surging indignation within her seemed to disappear as swiftly as it had arrived, leaving her weak, shaken, in no way ready to cope with his imminent attack.

'Grant,' she pleaded through trembling lips, barely conscious that she had spoken aloud.

His eyes were intent on her white, desperate face, the two patches of colour blazing in her cold cheeks, aflame against the green clouded despair in her eyes. 'Liza!' he moaned, and to her amazement suddenly caught her close, his strong hands slipping gently about her slender body, as if attempting to disperse the wildly fearful look she gave him.

'Liza,' he repeated, his arms restraining her when she would have pulled free of him, 'don't say a word until you've listened to me. I want to marry you. I don't care how many men you've known in the past. Last night I must have been a little crazy—you can put it down to plain jealousy if you like, but I love you, I want you, I can't let you go. This morning when I came to my senses, I rang to tell you, and the girl who answered said you'd gone, and didn't intend coming back. I've nearly been out of my mind! I didn't expect you'd ever come near the shop. I did ask Miss Russell to send you along if you did, and when you didn't turn up I was convinced I had lost you. It must have been sheer instinct which led me to your department, and just to see you standing there made me realise how much I cared. I swear I won't let you out of my sight again, so you'd better be prepared to marry me soon!'

'Grant . . .'

'Darling,' he interrupted grimly, tilting up her quivering

chin until his eyes stared down into her own, 'don't just keep on repeating my name. All I want to hear you say is yes!'

The same imperious Grant, yet how could she resist him? Wordlessly Liza nodded, a sob in her throat, her heart in her eyes as she gazed at him, 'I love you, darling,' she whispered with the first breath he allowed her after he stopped kissing her, minutes later.

'That first day I saw you,' he groaned, surveying her flushed face and tumbled hair with growing satisfaction, 'I knew I must have you. It's maybe too long afterwards to apologise for my deliberate attack, but on the spur of the moment it was the only way I could think of to get near you. And I was actually sitting here planning a ruthless campaign, designed to sweep aside all your defences, when news came about the fire. I was frantic, Liza, to think I had come so near losing you when I'd only just found you, then last night ... Oh, my darling, you must forgive me! Your past doesn't matter.'

'Grant.' There was a kind of glory in her face, and she wanted nothing more than to forget about everything except loving him. But first she must try to get certain things straight. There was no way she could match his generosity, but she owed him this. Besides, her father would have wanted it, Liza realised this now. 'That girl in my diaries wasn't me,' she said, ungrammatically, 'and Dan was my father.'

'Your father?'

'Yes.' Numbly Liza nodded. 'When I was a baby I couldn't pronounce Dad properly—it always came out as Dan. Sometimes, on the odd occasion, I still used it.'

'Look, Liza,' the paleness of her face alarmed him, 'you don't have to tell me anything.'

'I must,' she replied simply. 'Haven't you trusted me? My father, you see, got involved with this girl. She wasn't actually a girl, but a woman in her early thirties. She was married, only her husband had been away almost a year working on oil rigs on the other side of the world. I don't know if she and my father fell in love—they might have done, but anyway, I'd no idea things had gone so far until she came and told me about the baby. I can only remember now that I was shocked, and I shouldn't have been.'

Grant frowned, aware that some of the shock still remained, but he knew better than to stop her. 'Liza, in your diary you said, "The baby's lost, and perhaps just as well as there could have been no marriage." Then you went on—"Dan has left me and I'm heartbroken, especially as it could have been my fault." What did you mean?'

Liza replied starkly, 'She came and told me she'd got rid of the baby, just like that. Later a friend of hers confirmed it, that she'd been expecting one, that is. I hadn't even known about her relationship with my father. When he came in and more or less confessed and said he would take Lula out in the boat and sort things out, I think I must have gone slightly mad. I told them I never wanted to see either of them again. And I didn't.'

'Liza! God, darling, don't!' Protectively his arms tightened.

'Don't you see? Dan was never a good sailor, he relied on me. They went out on the lagoon, beyond the breakwater. A sudden squall blew up and I never saw them alive again.'

'Why did this woman have to tell you like that about the child, or even tell you at all?'

'I'm not sure,' Liza confessed, her eyes bright with unshed tears. 'Sometimes she used to taunt me, say I was too naive, that I'd never experienced life. Maybe she was right. I'd always been too absorbed with Dan's work, his books, to bother much with boy-friends. But I should have realised that he was a man and would want other friendships.'

'She could have been jealous, even though she was married to someone else. What did you do—afterwards?' Grant's voice was grim as, in retrospect, he considered her plight.

Liza shivered. 'Nothing. That seemed the most dreadful part of it. There was nothing I could do. I stayed for a few days at the Consulate and they helped me get back here. They were very kind, but there was no one I could really confide in. That's why, I suppose, I put it all down in my diary.'

'Worded so it would be difficult for anyone else reading it to guess the real truth?'

She nodded. 'To protect my father had seemed to become a habit since my mother died. And the girl had a husband who could have been hurt.'

'Darling,' Grant held her closer, 'you've got me now. You've told me all about it and it will pass. I'll look after you and I think, guessing the kind of man your father was from his books, he will be well content if I make you happy.'

'Yes.' A new gladness was invading Liza's heart, along with the man who held her. 'Oh, Grant, I didn't know what I was going to do when I thought you didn't want me. It was something like that week at Lynsend when you promised to come down and never came, only worse.'

'That was when I read your diary, and had never known such black misery in all my life. I couldn't face you!'

Unconsciously Liza exclaimed, 'It was the same when Paula suggested you loved Phoebe, only afterwards I couldn't bring myself to believe you'd caused her death.'

'Phoebe?' Grant's voice hardened incredulously. 'Liza, would you mind explaining?'

'I'm sorry, darling.' Liza felt herself go cold, wishing fervently that she'd never mentioned it. 'I think it was a mistake...'

'Liza!'

There was no evading the command in Grant's tone. Reluctantly she confessed, 'Paula merely told me that you were in love with Phoebe, and that she was driving your car and the brakes failed.'

'She told you that!' His eyes went icy. Then, as Liza nodded numbly, 'Phoebe was the last person! We didn't even care for each other very much. She knew about the faulty brakes, but apparently she and Adrian had quarrelled. Not an unusual occurrence,' he added wryly, 'but this time she was absolutely infuriated and rushed out and took my car which, unfortunately, my man had left out on the drive for the local garage to pick up. Obviously she had forgotten as she couldn't stop at the end of the drive to avoid a lorry. But I never loved her.'

'Then Paula...?'

'Paula's mind works strangely, Liza, it always did. If she thought you could help Adrian she wouldn't want you ever to think of me. This is partly why I've given her Lynsend. I can't allow her to intrude any more. Adrian, I'm afraid, must work out his own salvation. I think I've done all that's possible. We'll find another place, darling, somewhere. I don't care where, so long as you're happy.'

'Darling,' Liza felt oddly humble, 'you don't know how much I love you.' She felt terribly unhappy for Adrian, but she also knew a surge of relief. 'I love you,' she repeated again fervently, her eyes softly adoring.

'And I you. And for all the dark unhappiness I've suffered I'm going to demand a penalty. Liza,' his slight smile faded to a new, gentler tenderness, 'I tried to stay away in vain—I tried to punish you but only succeeded in hurting myself more. Don't you think I need a little commiseration, darling?'

'If you say so, Mr Latham!' Liza's heart felt suddenly lighter with a dawning delight, and her arms went up, wrapping tightly about the strong column of his neck, a vibrant excitement surging as his head bent. Then there was only the passionate pressure of his sensuous mouth on her lips, the urgent strength of his insistent body.

Neither of them so much as heard Mr Latham's secretary open the door, or her slight gasp of utter disbelief as she quickly closed it again.

Harlequin
Announces the
COLLECTION
EDITIONS
OF 1978

Harlequin's Collection 1

ANDREA BLAKE
**Night of
the Hurrica**

Harlequin's Collection 106   1.2$

ANNE WEALE
**If This
Is Love**

stories of special
beauty and significance

25 Beautiful stories of particular merit

In 1976 we introduced the first 100 Harlequin Collections — a selection of titles chosen from our best sellers of the past 20 years. This series, a trip down memory lane, proved how great romantic fiction can be timeless and appealing from generation to generation. Perhaps because the theme of love and romance is eternal, and, when placed in the hands of talented, creative, authors whose true gift lies in their ability to write from the heart, the stories reach a special level of brilliance that the passage of time cannot dim. Like a treasured heirloom, an antique of superb craftsmanship, a beautiful gift from someone loved, — these stories too, have a special significance that transcends the ordinary.

Here's your 1978 Harlequin Collection Editions . . .

More great Harlequin 1978 Collection Editions . . .

Poignant tales of love, conflict, romance and adventure

Elegant and sophisticated novels of
great romantic fiction . . .
12 All time best sellers.

Join the millions of avid Harlequin readers all over the world who delight in the magic of a really exciting novel.

From the library of Harlequin Presents all time best sellers — we are proud and pleased to make available the 12 selections listed here.

Combining all the essential elements you expect of great story telling, and bringing together your very favourite authors — you'll thrill to these exciting tales of love, conflict, romance, sophistication and adventure. You become involved with characters who are interesting, vibrant, and alive. Their individual conflicts, struggles, needs, and desires, grip you, the reader, until the final page.

Have you missed any of these *Harlequin Presents*..

Offered to you in the sequence in which they were originally printed — this is an opportunity for you to add to your Harlequin Presents . . . library.

This elegant and sophisticated series was first introduced in 1973, and has been a huge success ever since. The world's top romantic fiction authors combine glamour, exotic local dramatic and poignant love themes woven into gripping and absorbing plots to create an unique reading experience in each novel.

You'd expect to pay $1.75 or more for this calibre of best selling novel, — at only **$1.25 each,** Harlequin Presents are truly top value, top quality entertainment.

Don't delay — order yours today

Complete and mail this coupon today!